FREEZE BEFORE BURNING

A Sam Tate Mystery

by

Nikki Stern

445 Sayre Drive
Princeton, NJ 08540

Cover Design: Coverkitchen

ISBN: 978-0-9995487-6-9 (print book)
978-0-9995487-7-6 (ebook)

LCCN: 2021919754

Library of Congress Cataloging-in-Publication Data is on file with the Library of Congress.

Acknowledgements

Procedurals always require input from professionals. I had the help of several, beginning with James O'Sullivan. Detective O'Sullivan is a 20+ year veteran of the NYPD, fifteen of those years as detective. He is currently assigned to the Joint Terrorism Task Force. I can attest to his knowledge of procedure, his endless patience, and his sense of humor. Thanks also to Rob Messner, NYPD Assistant Deputy Commissioner (retired) and currently a criminal justice professor, for connecting me with both Jimmy and with Shiya Ribowsky's invaluable book, *Dead Center*, about working at New York's Office of the Chief Medical Examiner. And kudos to Tim Moran for getting the ball rolling.

Editors are the backbone of the process, and I had two. The talented writer Steve Axelrod, author of the Henry Kinnis mystery books, was appropriately intolerant of cheap language and lazy slang. He makes me a better writer. And Rachael Kowal, Managing Editor of SoHo Press, is as sharp-eyed and respectful as they come.

I continue to be awed and amazed by the cover creations by Coverkitchen. My dear friend Diana Ani Stokely remains my book project manager and website guru.

Special thanks to my cousins Judy and Frank Sherkow for their unwavering support, their voluminous knowledge about so many things, and Judy's eagle-eyed proofing. They have been my sounding board and my muses during this process, and I can't find words to express my gratitude except these I'm writing now.

White as snow
cold as ice
pale as dead.
—Anonymous

Nothing burns like the cold.
—George R.R. Martin

Chapter 1

Ed Rizzo slid his ample body into the ornate confessional, crossed himself, and pushed a strand of thinning hair off his forehead. "Forgive me, Father," he intoned, "for I have sinned, although I'm pretty sure God will cut me some slack even if my wife won't, if you take my meaning."

At ten in the morning, the sanctuary was deserted. Good. He didn't need anyone listening to his confession, which he unloaded to the figure who sat beside him in the confessional over the next ten minutes.

Even as he talked, he considered who might be on the other side of the grate. Rizzo couldn't make out the features of the man. He wondered if he'd landed the new priest. Maybe a younger person would make light of his transgressions, which mostly related to his perfectly legitimate reaction to his obnoxious neighbor, Frank Pagonis.

Rizzo had his justifications lined up. He hadn't survived more than a year of enforced quarantine with three kids and a demanding wife, never mind the missing paycheck for a while, only to put up with the stolen newspapers, a lawn mower returned with a bent blade, and a television loud enough to wake the dead.

"But when his dog, which, by the way, he refuses to leash and that's against the law, went and dug up my tomato plants, yeah, I sprayed some stuff on whatever the mutt left. Not enough to kill the animal, you understand. He can't help it if he has a jerk for an owner. I would have sprayed his owner's food if I could have. The point I'm making is, the dog got sick, but it didn't die, okay?"

Rizzo cocked his head, thinking he might have heard a faint sigh.

"Now he's coming around with a pile of vet bills and talking about suing me. I told him to take his threats and shove them. I tell you, Padre, I am this close to beating that smug face or maybe twisting that scrawny neck of his. My wife claims that kind of thinking is sinful. I don't think it's as bad as doing the deed. I haven't told her about poisoning the dog, but sparing her the details isn't the same as lying, is it?"

Nothing. The guy had probably fallen asleep. The confessional was stuffy, and Rizzo experienced a touch of claustrophobia. Time to move things along.

"If you can just suggest a penance to perform, I'll get it covered. Then I can be on my way."

He stopped talking, suddenly aware of the silence, how absolute and enveloping it was. The noises of the city street outside had receded. He could hear himself breathing.

"Hey, Father? You all right in there?" Rizzo scratched the grill dividing the two sides of the confessional. His head was pounding now, and he felt vaguely dizzy.

"I know I've been yakking a lot. How about we wrap this up, okay?" Again, no response. It occurred to Rizzo that the other man hadn't said a word the entire time. What if the good father had suffered a heart attack?

He hoisted his bulk off the narrow bench and pushed himself out of the tiny space. The other side of the confessional had its own entrance. He rapped on the door, then tried the handle, more out of instinct than anything else. It turned in his hand, and he pulled.

The black-garbed figure sat with head bowed, hands folded in his lap as if in prayer or contemplation. Or asleep. Rizzo put a tentative hand on the man's shoulder. With a sigh like a punctured balloon, the black-robed figure tipped sideways off the bench, fell to the floor, and rolled like a blow-up toy.

Startled, Rizzo jumped back. Stay cool, he told himself.

He bent over with an *umph* and put two fingers to the priest's throat to search for a pulse. He expected to feel cold, not the scalding heat that burned his skin.

"Jesus Christ!" he yelled, forgetting for a moment where he was. He waved his blistered hand in the air and hopped around until a wave of nausea stopped.

With his foot, he nudged the body so that it rolled onto its back. He stared, speechless for once, at the face of the priest. Then he stepped farther back, pulled out his cell phone, punched in 9-1-1, and gave his report to the dispatcher in a calm, measured tone.

He agreed to wait for the police and medical authorities just outside the church. He even accepted the suggestion that he might dissuade others from entering until help arrived.

Without looking again at the body of the priest, Ed Rizzo crossed himself. He walked slowly to the front door, stepped into the fresh air, and threw up.

Chapter 2

Sam strolled along Thirtieth Avenue looking for familiar places from her childhood. The Greek diner was still there. So was the pizza place. The pasture-raised barbecue joint was new and so was the multistory apartment building just around the corner.

The faces were more diverse as well, a cultural melting pot that added to the predominantly Italian and Greek population she recalled. And younger; she noticed fewer black-clad grandmothers with shopping bags filled with fresh produce. They'd been replaced by twenty-to-thirty-year-olds with phones on and heads down.

Here, too, were more homeless people than she had anticipated, despite efforts to move them into shelters or over to the expressway underpass. They lay in the doorways of the shuttered stores, their funk mixing with the smell of spice, meat, and auto fumes.

Some things hadn't changed. Her aunt Rosa's house, where she'd unpacked her bags just yesterday, looked almost exactly as she remembered it from her childhood. The upstairs apartment had been remodeled, and the stove in the main kitchen was new. Her aunt had aged after twenty-seven years, but she still possessed the same resilience, an up-tempo fatalism that worked for her.

Yet Sam felt unsettled and out of place. She went back to visit the house she'd lived in as a child and scarcely recognized it. New facade, a miniature English garden in place of the postage-stamp-size lawn. She imagined the interior had been gutted and reconfigured as an open floor plan.

Hard to believe she'd grown up on this block, lulled into a false sense of security by the familiar rituals of childhood. That she sat once in church, attended public school, played with friends, and celebrated holidays with her father's noisy, loving family. That she'd lived a normal life, not that she knew what normal meant anymore.

Sam stopped at an outdoor café that advertised coffee made from ethically sourced beans from around the globe. She chose Café Brasileiro made with sweetened condensed milk and paired it with a fruit-filled wedding cookie. She turned her face to the warm October sun and let her shoulders drop.

She couldn't remember the last time she'd relaxed, even for a minute. She'd been at her current job for six months when the pandemic struck. At that point, she was coming off the high of solving a triple homicide. The quarantine precipitated a spike in domestic violence. She masked up and made house calls or sat at her desk fielding complaints. At night, she ate dinner alone in her dilapidated rental cottage on a dead-end road and obsessed over the past. Or she thought about FBI Special Agent Terry Sloan and wondered if he were thinking about her.

The coffee and cookie combination produced a not-unpleasant sugar rush that brought her back into the moment. Dr. Putnam, her on-again, off-again therapist, had suggested she try to live in the now. She hadn't quite gotten the hang of it.

She finished her midmorning treat and resumed her walk. Before long, she found herself in front of St.

Joseph's Roman Catholic Church. While her family belonged to Our Lady of Mount Carmel, Colleen, Sam's mother, would sometimes slip off to pray at St. Joe's. She told Sam the visits brought her comfort, yet she always returned home with tears in her eyes.

Today the modest church was bathed in light from both the bright sun and the flashing lights of the two cruisers and the EMT vehicle parked in front. Uniformed figures swarmed the entrance like carpenter ants. The familiar crackle of a police radio punctuated the babble of voices. A small crowd of gawkers filled the opposite sidewalk, prevented from crossing the street by serious-faced patrolmen.

"What's going on?" she inquired of a stout woman in a turquoise dress.

"Someone's been killed," the woman responded. "They say it was the new priest." She crossed herself.

"Not Father Clemons!" the young mother next to her exclaimed. "He was so nice."

A tall man standing nearby added, "I heard he was burned." More murmuring and crossing from the bystanders.

Burned? Sam wondered. She looked around, sniffed the air. No smell that suggested a fire, no trucks to supplement the police and medical vehicles.

"Tate? Sam Tate? What the hell, girl?" The voice, its familiar Appalachian roots overlaid with a New York dialect, pulled Sam around.

"Is that Ron? Ron Zielinski? Oh my God, it is you!" Her former partner's younger brother was grinning ear to ear. He wore pressed slacks and a neat blue blazer that just fit his broad shoulders and chest. Same build as his brother, more fireplug than willow. Same shaved head, bushy eyebrows, and hazel eyes with a couple of added lines on each side. A few years older than Sam, which put him into his forties.

Like his older sibling, Ron Zielinski was from Nashville and part of a family of police officers. Unlike Larry, Ron had headed to New York as soon as he graduated high school, earned a degree from John Jay College of Criminal Justice, joined the NYPD, and worked his way up the chain of command. She'd met him a couple of times in Nashville, mostly during holidays. She'd listen to his stories about working in Manhattan with a mix of nostalgia and pain. No one she worked with knew she'd lived in neighboring Queens the first nine years of her life.

Sam walked over, trying to decide which post-COVID greeting to use, a decision Ron settled by pulling her into a brief embrace.

"You look like you've been holding back time," he marveled.

"And you look like you're moving ahead. Is that a detective shield?"

"Manhattan South Homicide Squad. Just took the sergeant's exam. We'll see. For sure it would please the wife."

"Sounds terrific, Ron. What are you doing in Queens?"

The grin faded. "Dead body inside the church could be connected to a case I'm working back in Manhattan. This promises to be one of the bizarre ones. The homicide detective from Queens North called me to see for myself."

"And here I thought the precincts were territorial."

"That's only on the cop shows. We get along in real life, helped by some ongoing bureaucratic restructuring. The detective and I go back a ways. Now it's my turn. What are you doing here?"

"I'm visiting," she replied quickly. She didn't want to mention family or her real reason for returning. As far as most everyone knew, her parents had died early in her life, after which she was raised by a loving aunt and uncle in Delaware.

Larry and his brother were both seasoned detectives. Maybe they'd already come up on the truth. Maybe it didn't matter.

She brought herself back in time to catch the tail end of his question.

"... working in that Podunk County job you landed after you left that other Podunk County job in Tennessee?"

"Still there," she said with a smile. For now, her inner voice added. "Here I am on vacation, and you're on a case that has brought you across the river. Color me curious."

She saw him start to shut down and raised her hands in mock surrender. "I get it," she said. "You can't say anything."

Her attention was diverted by the sight of a man and a woman over Zielinski's shoulder. The woman was tall and thin. Late twenties, although her dour expression added years, as did her hairstyle. Who wore their hair in a bun anymore? No makeup, minimal jewelry, a mask around her neck. Her somber pantsuit seemed more appropriate for a federal agent than an NYPD officer.

The woman's dark gray eyes narrowed as she walked up. Sam thought of thunder clouds.

Her companion made a very different impression. Tall and well proportioned, he radiated warmth and good humor. He'd dressed more casually, just a blazer over jeans. Gold shield on his belt, and a lapel pin Sam couldn't place.

She ran down a quick checklist of his appealing attributes. Thick hair flecked with silver, check. Deep chocolate eyes that crinkled at the corners, check. Strong chin covered by a trace of beard that suggested he'd missed a day of shaving, check. A slightly crooked nose and small scar on one cheek that identified him as a tough guy, check. No wedding ring, check.

The very definition of tall, dark, and handsome. Worthy of a romance novel cover but not worthy of all the attention she seemed to be giving him. Sam flushed and looked down at her hands to compose herself.

Hot Guy stopped in front of them. "Hey, Zielinski," he said, "thanks for coming." His cadence suggested outer borough origins or maybe Long Island.

Sam caught herself staring again and took a deep breath. Zielinski's knowing smile seemed to say, *He does that to nearly everybody.* So did the female detective's obvious displeasure, which worked on Sam like ice water.

"Danny Carlisle, as I live and breathe!" Zielinski crowed. "Queen's finest homicide detective."

"Hardest working, for sure." Carlisle pointed to his companion. "Meet Chloe Nichols, youngest detective we've ever welcomed to Queens North. I'm serving as mentor slash big brother, at least until she complains."

"Shouldn't take long." Zielinski laughed and smiled at the younger woman. "I remember hearing about you a couple years back, Detective Nichols."

"Who didn't?" Carlisle replied. "She chased down a two-hundred-eighty-pound suspect and tackled him to the ground. Came back to work in no time."

"And now you're a detective," Sam noted. "Well done."

Nichols folded her arms across her chest. "Thanks," she said.

Carlisle jumped in with a twinkle in his eye. "We haven't met. Don't blame Ron. He forgets his manners at times."

"This is Sam Tate, my brother's former partner back in Nashville."

Sam raised her hand. "Pleased to meet you, Detectives."

Carlisle put his fist to his heart, the greeting a cross between *Star Trek* and *Wakanda Forever*. Everyone was coming up with new ways to acknowledge one another, now that COVID had rendered handshakes less desirable. Except Nichols, who managed only a small head bob.

"Nice to meet you, too," Carlisle said. "I wonder why your name rings a bell." He mulled it over for a couple of seconds, then put a finger to his head. "Oh, yeah. Nashville detective turned county sheriff who caught a serial killer the FBI had been chasing for years." He looked at her more closely. "You still in Tennessee, Sheriff?"

"Talbot County, Maryland. And it's lieutenant now, not sheriff. But you can call me Sam, Detective." Her smile felt stiff.

"And you can call me Dan, which I prefer, or Danny, which apparently everyone else does." He glanced at Nichols.

"Detective Nichols is fine," she said flatly. She looked down at her phone. "We're cleared to go in now."

"Good," Carlisle said. "I want to have a word with the MLI."

"Stands for medicolegal investigator, who works with the medical examiner's office," Carlisle added for Sam's benefit. "We three ought to head inside."

Sam took the hint.

"I need to get back to my aunt. I think she's making her famous Italian wedding soup for lunch, even though it's seventy degrees and I offered to take her out. Nice to see you, Ron. Detective Carlisle, Detective Nichols, good to meet you both."

"How long are you here, Sam?" Zielinski asked.

"Between two and three weeks. It's a little open-ended."

"Sounds like it. You got time for a beer later?"

"I can make time. When and where?"

"Meet me back here at seven thirty," Zielinski suggested. "You mind if we head into Manhattan? Maybe I can get Margarite to join us."

"Is that your wife?" Sam asked.

Carlisle chuckled. "His work wife. Detective Margarite Lopez is a fellow homicide detective."

"You want to join us, Danny, Detective Nichols?" Zielinski asked. "Could be fun."

Nichols didn't appear interested in fun. "I gotta get home," she said.

Sam expected Carlisle to beg off so he could join his undoubtedly beautiful wife and beautiful children for a beautiful evening. Instead, he suggested they all go to McSorley's.

Zielinski looked skeptical. "Not too touristy?"

"McSorley's is an institution, Ron. Lieutenant Tate is a tourist. She's also a cop who would appreciate both the history and the atmosphere."

"And the burgers." Zielinski patted his stomach. "Okay, then, Sam. See you back here."

"Can you answer one question before I take off?" she asked. Without waiting for an answer, she continued. "I heard the victim might have been burned. But I didn't see any signs of a fire."

Nichols shook her head.

"She's a cop, Chloe," Carlisle responded. He turned to Sam. "The precinct detective said the MLI was playing it close to the vest. We know the victim has burns inside his mouth and all the way down his throat. Which is why I called Ron."

"A chemical burn?" Sam couldn't help asking. "Lighter fluid? Acid? A cleaning solvent?"

Carlisle shook his head. "More like frostbite."

Zielinski nodded. "Just like my victim."

"Frostbite?" Sam was incredulous. "What, did the guy eat dry ice?"

No one responded.

"Holy shit!" she said.

Zielinski looked grim. "Nothing holy about it."

Chapter 3

"How are you doing, Tate? Did I catch you in the middle of something?"

"Women's work," Sam said and laughed. She sat cross-legged on the couch in the front parlor of her aunt's house, her laptop open. She'd been scrolling through work emails, looking for clues about her future hidden within the mundane communiques, when her phone had rung. Rosa was busying herself with some sewing repairs. The woman never lacked for projects. Perhaps that was how she kept her life so ordered.

Sam rose with an "excuse me." She pretended not to notice Rosa's sly smile as she padded up the stairs.

"So," she said, beaming at her phone, "no FaceTime?"

"Nah. I'm on the move, in between the office and a rare in-person meeting. You'll have to make do with my seductive baritone. How's New York?"

"It's the same and different," she said, settling on the bed in the guest room. "Does that make sense? I'm remembering a lot and failing to remember a lot more. Not surprising. I was only nine when I left."

"How's your aunt?"

"She's as I remember her in a lot of ways. She's been sharing tidbits with me about our lives. I'm not pushing her. I should say, we're not pushing each other. I don't want to ..." She swallowed to loosen her tight throat.

"You're making up for lost time, Sam. Should I ask how you're sleeping?"

Sam had been having nightmares that began six or seven years earlier. They increased in frequency when she was stressed and especially when she was working a homicide. Details of the case intertwined with deeply buried memories about her childhood. She was seeing a therapist Terry had recommended, although "seeing" meant online conversations.

"The good news is, I haven't had a nightmare in over a week. The bad news is that my conscious mind won't slow down."

"You've got a lot to process. I don't guess you've gone back to Antun's."

"Not yet."

Antun's was the landmark Queen's wedding hall where a gunman had shot and killed her father and brother and left her mother with a traumatic brain injury when Sam was just nine.

The day of the shooting, Sam had walked up the aisle with the rest of the wedding party, delirious with joy. She'd passed a man in a brown suit, someone she thought she knew. Later, she would insist she'd seen that man stand and raise a gun. The idea there might have been a second shooter at the ceremony was never considered by any of the adults who interviewed her later. No one could or would corroborate the story of a grieving nine-year-old whose family had been destroyed.

For years she tried to put the incident out of her mind. Yet she kept replaying some version of that day, filling in details even as the nascent cop in her recognized the problem with trusting memories.

Fortunately, Terry believed her version of events. So did the one surviving member of the original wedding party they'd tracked down who recalled seeing the brown-suited man on another occasion. Even the therapist Sam saw back in Tennessee had come around to her way of thinking.

Three months later, the therapist was dead and so was Arthur Randolph, the man who'd spent twenty-five years in a mental institution after his arrest for the shooting. Terry discovered through law enforcement connections that someone had been looking at sealed testimony related to the shooting.

Then Sam met Sean Parker at a gallery opening in St. Michaels, Maryland.

A well-connected man running for the U.S. Senate, Parker looked vaguely familiar. At first Sam decided he was generically handsome. It wasn't until the second encounter, when he briefly removed his tinted glasses, that Sam experienced the shock of her adult life. He had her eyes, the unique shade of green, the shape. It was as if she were looking into a mirror.

She became obsessed with learning more about Sean Parker. She especially wanted to know if he was a part of her hidden past. Did he know her mother? Was he a relative? Was he at the wedding? The more she tried to find out, the more questions she had.

"Would Rosa go to Antun's with you?" Terry asked.

Sam plugged herself back into the conversation. "She's in her late seventies, Terry. Her brother and son were murdered right in front of her there. That's a big ask." She hesitated. "I showed her a picture of Sean Parker. She had no memory of him. She did say he looked like someone from my mother's side of the family."

"I'm sorry."

They paused.

"When do you finish your—?"

"Any word on the sheriff's plans to—?"

Terry's laugh eased the knot in her stomach.

"You first," she said.

"What's the news at work?"

"Same old, same old."

"I'm sorry, Sam. I know you were hoping to take Sheriff Donohue's place when he went on leave."

"Tanner Reed is a good man and a pillar of the community. Me, I've changed jobs three times in ten years. Doesn't allow for a lot of employer confidence. Never mind. Let's talk about you."

"I expect to be the proud owner of a Master's in Criminal Justice from George Washington University by Christmas. Just about the time I move out of field work and into supervisory work, which will make my knees very happy." He laughed again.

She sensed his pride and his relief. Terry had spent the past year and a half studying and performing both supervisory and field work for the FBI's Criminal Victims Unit. His division had been stretched to the limit. Stress was taking a toll on all of them.

The quarantine had made it almost impossible to connect in any way but digitally. Late last summer, they got together for the first time in nearly a year. The reunion was sweet but also a little awkward, made more so by Sam's awareness that they were at different places in their lives. While he made things happen for himself in Washington, she stayed out in the country, working a job with a built-in glass ceiling.

They hadn't been able to reconnect in person since the one time, though she desperately wanted to make it happen. Instead, they texted nearly every day like friends and former partners as well as whatever they were trying to be now.

As if reading her mind, he said, "Sam, is there anything you want to talk about? The past, the present, or ..." he let the sentence trail off.

"How's this for present? I was walking down the street when I ran into the younger brother of my old partner Larry Zielinski. He's an NYPD detective working a couple of homicides with a shared and very weird MO. It appears the victims might have died from being forced to swallow dry ice. Ron had a case in Manhattan last week, and as of this morning, there's a similar homicide in Queens."

"Lord, that sounds ghastly. Are they thinking serial killer?"

"I don't know if they're ready to label it as such." Sam hesitated. "Or whether they'd call in the Feds if they did."

"NYPD is pretty well equipped to handle whatever comes their way without requesting our help," Terry observed. "But dry ice as a weapon? That appeals to the behavioral analyst in me."

"I'm going to dinner with Ron and the other detectives this evening." *One of whom is smoking hot*, she found herself thinking. "Maybe they'll share some details with a fellow cop."

"I hope you're not going to get pulled in, Sam. You're supposed to be on vacation. Not that I believe you're going to take too much time for yourself."

"Come on! I went for a nice walk this morning."

"Uh-huh. And walked up on a crime scene your first full day there."

"I'm here to see my aunt and jog some memories, Terry. That's all, I promise. Besides, I'm just a lawman from rural Maryland. I doubt anyone's gonna welcome my involvement."

"I don't know about that. My guess is a good-looking serial-killer-catching outsider might appeal even to jaded New York detectives."

"Is that your gut instinct talking?" Sam asked. She meant it as a joke, but Terry didn't laugh.

"Just watch your step, okay?"

As usual, Terry's instincts turned out to be reliable.

Chapter 4

McSorley's Old Ale House is a New York City saloon in Manhattan's East Village. Founded in 1854, the bar has welcomed a variety of famous figures from Abe Lincoln and Teddy Roosevelt to John Lennon and Woody Guthrie. Newspaper articles cover the walls and sawdust blankets the floor, an homage to the days of full spittoons and customers with bad aim. Seven regulars have their ashes interred behind the bar.

One of the last "men only" pubs, McSorley's finally admitted women in 1970. Twenty-odd years later, it welcomed its first female bartender, the daughter of the late owner. The pandemic forced a temporary closing, but loyal customers came back as soon as the doors opened.

Ron wrapped up his brief history at the bar, raising his voice over the din as they entered. The place was packed, every table occupied, the noise at rock concert level. It was as loud as might be expected of a popular Irish pub. Again, Sam thought about what it meant to be almost on the other side of a life-threatening pandemic. Maybe this was it, a room of weary, thirsty, mostly male New Yorkers looking for companionship, connection, beer, and burgers.

"There's Margarite." Ron moved down the bar to a small table for four to greet a sloe-eyed woman with a mask around her neck. She was small and lean with a strong face and a no-nonsense air about her. To her standard detective apparel of black blazer, white shirt, dark jeans, she'd added a delicate gold crucifix and a couple of small studs along one earlobe.

Sam smiled; her own ear piercings were her small act of rebellion.

She extended her fist across the table by way of greeting and brushed a strand of short, dark hair off her face.

"Detective Margarite Lopez," she said before Ron could open his mouth. "Margarite, not Margarita or Marge or Maggie, or, God forbid, Mags. If you prefer, you can call me Lopez." She spoke quickly. "I should warn you, my partner here sent me a novel's worth of texts about you this afternoon. I filled in the rest from the web. Your reputation precedes you."

She laughed at Sam's expression. "We're detectives, Lieutenant. We always do our research."

"I wouldn't expect anything less," Sam replied. "And since we're off duty, you can call me Sam or even Tate." She hadn't anticipated being vetted before what she assumed was a social dinner. It rankled, just a little.

"Got it," Lopez said with a smile. "No Saunders?" she asked Zielinski. "That's the Manhattan Precinct detective who caught last week's case," she added

"He's on leave, thanks to a concrete curb he didn't notice before he stepped off and went flying," her partner said. "The detective from 114 in Queens won't be here, either."

"Good. Just us homicide dicks then." She grinned at Sam. "I gather you met TDH?"

"Come again?"

"Danny Carlisle, talk, dark, and handsome in the flesh." Lopez noted Sam's embarrassed flush. "Don't worry about it. Anyone with a pulse would notice." She twisted in her seat. "Where is our charming detective?"

Danny Carlisle chose that moment to make his entrance. He'd combed his hair and changed his shirt. The stubble remained.

"Greetings, gang," he said, pulling out the chair next to Sam's and nearly sideswiping a waiter in the process. "I see McSorley's has returned to its pre-pandemic insanity. Hey, Lopez, how goes it?"

"I'm good, Danny. You know everyone here."

"Yep. I had the pleasure of meeting Lieutenant Sam Tate this morning." He played it low-key, a lopsided grin, a slight twinkle in the eye. Somehow these worked on Sam more than any obvious flirtation might. She hoped she could keep from blushing.

"Detective Carlisle. Nice to see you." She scraped her chair over as he pulled his out. Nevertheless, their arms brushed. She jumped at the contact and found three pair of eyes on her.

"It's not you, it's me," she said with a self-deprecating laugh. "I'm not used to so many people so close together."

"Wait until you get on the subway," Zielinski told her. "I don't know that I'll ever take my mask off down there."

"No shit," Lopez said. "Ron, do you remember that drunk guy we had to arrest last year? He threw up in the scarf he was using as a face covering. That was above and beyond."

That story led to another. Sam tried to relax, but Carlisle's physical presence had an effect on her that she couldn't blame solely on months of quarantine.

Zielinski recommended they order. "The place is famous for its ale," he said. "They've added some other options to the menu if you want to go that way."

"McSorley's dark ale is fine," Sam said. "And the burger with onions." She'd done her research as well.

Her companions nodded their approval. Carlisle put up a hand, pulled over a waiter, and put in an order. "Four burgers with onions, two pitchers of dark ale. To start." He winked at Sam.

Sam had no intention of being quizzed on her peripatetic career or her brief turn in the media spotlight. While they waited for the beer to arrive, she peppered them with questions. How long had Zielinski and Lopez been homicide detectives? (Ten and seven years, respectively.) Had either of them ever worked with Carlisle before? ("We came up together," Zielinski replied, while Lopez responded with a terse, "more than once.") Had the homicide rate gone up or down during the pandemic? (Down, until recently.)

When the pitchers arrived, Carlisle filled the glasses and proposed a toast. "To old friendships and new partnerships." Everyone drank. The back of Sam's neck prickled. She didn't sense danger but maybe another kind of ambush.

"Ron has a lot of good things to say about your experience, Sam," Lopez began. "One of the highest close rates at Nashville PD. The case of the serial killer with the wedding fetish you worked with the FBI. The high-class psycho grifter you caught three months into your new job. That's a hell of a record to amass inside a decade."

"Just lucky, I guess."

"More than luck," Zielinski put in. "The pandemic hit us hard. The Manhattan Precinct that caught the Paulson case is down two detectives. Same with our squad, one of them ..." he stopped to clear his throat.

"One permanently. I took the liberty of talking with my CO about you this afternoon."

"Talking you up, he means," Lopez added. "He thinks you're some kind of superstar."

"Ron, you shouldn't have ..."

"Let me finish," Zielinski insisted. "No one is asking anything of you that you don't want to offer. You're on vacation; I get it. But you're a fresh set of eyes we could use on a case that promises to be one of the bizarre ones. If you're interested and willing to listen, contribute, offer any insight while you're here and only if you have the time, we'd like to have your assistance. No more time than you can give."

"No one's offering you a shield," Lopez put in. "Those are hard to get." Laughter around the table. "But we might be able to get you a stipend, right Ron?"

He nodded.

Sam looked down at her plate. Notwithstanding Terry's cautionary advice and her own early-warning system, she felt blindsided. She found it hard to believe the mighty NYPD needed help from a county cop, even one who'd solved two serial killer cases in a row. If it was a publicity stunt, she wanted no part of it.

On the other hand, the Queens connection provided an opportunity. Carlisle was too young to have been working in 1994, but he might know someone who was on duty back then, someone who might have responded to a call about a shooting at Antun's. Besides, the case appealed to her. She even liked the idea of being part of a team instead of its leader.

"You're all okay with this?" she asked.

"Maybe we don't want to put the lieutenant on the spot," Carlisle interjected. "We might not even need her considerable talents. Let's not forget, I just hopped on this bandwagon. I'd like a little time to get up to speed if no one minds."

"How much time do you need, Danny?" Lopez asked. The question bristled with sharp edges.

"Hold up," Sam said. "I'm sure you all have a lot to talk about. Now, I can listen and ask questions. I can stay and keep quiet. I can also leave right now, and you can divvy up my burger. Whatever you all want."

"Come on, Sam," Zielinski pleaded. "Four heads are better than one."

"Good. I really didn't want to give up my burger." She got a laugh on that one. "But I'm going to take notes, if you don't mind." She pulled out a small pad and pen, a habit she developed back in Nashville.

"I've been over this so much I have it practically memorized," Lopez said. "Our Manhattan victim was a bartender and part-time actor named Grant Paulson. Twenty-five, Caucasian, moved to New York from Peoria five years ago, no known enemies, no outstanding warrants, in a committed relationship. He worked at a Times Square establishment called the Salty Peanut and no, they don't use dry ice in their drinks."

"How did you figure out the method of death?" Sam asked.

"It was a team effort. One of the cleaners complained she felt dizzy. The responding officers pulled everyone outside. The one who remained with the body became disoriented. A clever EMT threw open the doors and called DOH—the Department of Health—who showed up in full hazmat. They picked up traces of CO2 coming from the body. So did the medicolegal investigator when he was let in. And before you ask, this wasn't the carbon dioxide that the body releases postmortem. Decomp hadn't set in; the bartender was seen alive two hours before his body was found."

"He didn't inhale the gas?"

Zielinski shook his head. "Not enough to kill him."

The burgers arrived. Sam took a bite, trying not to think about what dry ice might do to the inside of someone's mouth. "I didn't realize someone could die from swallowing dry ice."

"We're not talking about a small amount like you'd find in a drink," Zielinski said. "The stuff comes in ten-pound blocks and Paulson may have taken in all of it. Whoever did this worked quickly. When the ice hit the stomach, it caused freezer burns to the lining. As it warmed up—it doesn't melt, by the way; it sublimates—it turned back to gas. The stomach blew up like a balloon, causing gastrointestinal perforation. That caused a whole lot of messy leaking into neighboring organs as well as internal bleeding and—"

"An agonizing death," Sam finished. She pushed her plate away, her appetite gone.

"The MLI drew a lot of the same conclusions about our priest, subject to the autopsy," Carlisle said. "Burning, blowing up, bleeding, the whole shebang."

"What else did you find out about the priest, Danny?" Lopez asked.

"I talked to the senior cleric at St. Joe's, Father Sacculi. He was upset, no surprise. Father Thomas Clemons was thirty-two, originally from Buffalo, served a small parish outside Boston before arriving here seven months ago. Popular with adults and kids, athletic, that sort of thing. Father Sacculi figured him for shortstop on the church baseball team. Oh, and he liked to listen to a true crime podcast called *Deep Freeze*."

"What?" Zielinski and Lopez spoke in unison, their attention fully directed to Carlisle.

"It's a thing right now," Carlisle said. "Lots of cable shows, hundreds of podcasts. This one is especially popular because it gets its listeners involved in cold cases."

"My seventy-eight-year-old aunt likes the show," Sam said. "She listens twice a week like clockwork. Talks about the hosts as if they're part of the Justice League."

"Sam, did Zielinski tell you anything about our Manhattan victim?" Lopez asked.

"Just the basics: age, occupation, preliminary cause and method of death. Why?"

"According to his significant other, Grant had three fixations: the theater; his bicycle, which he rode all over the city; and a true crime podcast he listened to religiously—that was the word his partner used—called *Deep Freeze*."

The chill that blew through the bar could have been caused by the door that swung open to admit a crowd of revelers. Somehow, Sam didn't think so.

Chapter 5

"No!" Sam yelled.

Fortunately, it came out as a squeak, further muffled by the floral comforter she'd pulled over her head as if to shield herself from the terrifying images.

She grabbed hold of the remnants of the dream before it evaporated. The young Sam, then known as Sophia, was standing with her brother's wedding party. She wore the pink dress made just for her and just for that day. All at once, she couldn't see, couldn't breathe. A cold smoke surrounded them, burning her throat, blocking her view. Through the vapors she saw the rest of the wedding party, including her cousin Johnny; her adored older brother, Stefan; and his intended, Nicole. They'd been frozen solid, even the priest, his face set in a terrifying rictus.

The morning light coming through the sheer curtains gave lie to her terrors but not the knowledge that her frightening dreams were back. Current events usually shaped the reveries in which old memories took new form. Here she was with family, or what was left of it, not far from the venue where she watched her loved ones get shot, about to be drawn into a gruesome homicide case.

It might have been something she ate. She was no novice when it came to drinking, but the combination of beer, burger, and onions could have ignited a serious case of nightmare-inducing indigestion. Or she was affected by the heady excitement of talking shop and shooting the breeze with a group of new colleagues.

Or maybe she'd been affected because she sat so close to one person in particular whose presence gave Sam a light-headed feeling unrelated to alcohol.

The scent of French toast, bacon, and coffee lured her down the stairs and into the kitchen, cell phone in hand. The way her aunt was feeding her, Sam would have to double the miles on her daily run and add interval training on top of that. Not that she minded. Food was often the simplest, most direct way to communicate. She and Rosa were reaching across decades and a lifetime of sorrow to reconnect.

She ought to bake a casserole for Terry, she thought. Or for her mother, even though any hope of interaction had diminished during the quarantine that kept Sam standing outside the older woman's care facility. When Sam finally got back inside, she found Colleen Russo faded and confined to bed.

Maybe she could cook for all the people she'd forgotten how to reach, or failed to reach when she allowed the lockdown to pull her deep within herself, where she could stew over a twenty-seven-year-old tragedy, a gunman in a brown suit, a man who looked familiar ...

Coffee. She needed coffee and some food and most definitely a sense of purpose that didn't trap her in the past. She shook her head.

Rosa looked up. "You okay, *cara*?" she asked

"Yeah, just looking forward to my wakeup drink." She headed to the coffee pot, poured herself a generous mug, inhaled, and drank with a sigh. "Ah, much better."

"Your uncle Jimmy always preferred caffeine to alcohol after a night out. He didn't believe in that old saying about the hair of the dog that bit you." She chuckled. "Did you have fun last night with your detective friends?"

Sam had mentioned running into her partner's brother without providing any details. "I did," she said. She took another swallow of coffee, then looked up to see her aunt eyeing her from her position at the stove. "What?"

"Sit down, I made French toast for you," her aunt said. She plopped a plate in front of her niece, then asked with an air of nonchalance, "So, are you going to help out with that strange case they're probably all working on?"

Sam didn't have to fake her surprise. "I'm sorry, what strange case?"

Rosa huffed, a plosive sound that went with her eye roll. "Oh, please. Where do you think you are and who do you think you're talking to? I read, I listen, I know things. You don't think I heard about the priest in the confessional over at St. Joseph's? Not exactly a natural death, what with the ice burns and all. Take a look." She tapped a copy of *The New York Post* that sat on the tiny kitchen table. "It's also in the *Daily News*, but I have to read that online since they stopped printing the paper."

Sam snatched up the tabloid. "Cold-Hearted Killing," the headline screamed and just below: "Queens Priest Victim in Bizarre Killing."

Oh, shit, she thought. *The team is not gonna like this.*

She skimmed the article. Unnamed insiders and confidential sources supplied the information, along with a mega-dose of eyewitness input. Something about freezer burns, nothing about dry ice and nothing, thank

God, about a similar homicide in Manhattan less than a week earlier.

Her aunt stood over her shoulder and pointed to the picture of St. Joseph's, not that Sam could have missed it. "Right in our neighborhood," she said.

Sam wasn't sure if she was terrified or thrilled. Maybe a little of each.

"Rosa, even if I wanted to get involved, and I don't because I'm here to visit you, it would not be possible." Sam balked as the words left her mouth. Zielinski and Lopez indicated they'd already spoken to their CO about using her as a consultant.

Her aunt poo-pooed her remarks. "First of all, they'd be crazy not to want to hear from someone with your serial killer experience." She sounded like she was channeling Terry. "Second of all, it's not like I need or expect you to be babysitting me every minute of the day. I got a lot on my plate, you know."

"I know, Rosa. I just thought—"

"Your father was the master of multitasking," her aunt went on. "Running his construction business, holding off the competition, and that included certain underworld types back in the eighties and nineties. Teaching Sunday school, coaching Little League. Pete did it all."

For a fraction of a second, she looked sad, defeated. Then it passed. "The point is," she said, "he always went where he was needed. And so will you."

Sam's phone buzzed. A text from Zielinski.

Did you see today's news?

This was followed by three yelling emojis and the symbols &#%!

She typed back:

Saw the Post. There's more?

Five seconds later, her phone rang.

"It's everywhere," Zielinski began before she'd said a word. "New York 1, WBS-FM, every damn online, print, and local morning show you can think of. Media is on it like a dog with a bone. I'd like to know who supplied them with their information. The only positive is that no one has linked the dead priest to the Paulson murder. Yet. But if there's a leak ..." He let out another expletive.

"Lopez is going over what we know about the bartender this morning to see if there might be other intersecting points between the two victims besides some interest in true crime. Like Paulson dated Clemson's cousin or Clemson played baseball with Paulson's brother. Or they met up at an Arby's and decided to travel on a cross-country trip. Maybe something will turn up when she compares notes with Carlisle or Nichols."

"How can I help, Ron?" Sam asked. Out of the corner of her eye, she saw Rosa give a thumbs up.

"If you have some time, how about you drop by at one p.m.? I'll introduce you around and we can grab some grub and sit down with Lopez to go over what we have. I want to find out more about this podcast and schedule a meeting with the two hosts—not to sucker punch them. They might have relevant information. Maybe your aunt can get you up to speed on the show, seeing as she's a fan."

"I'm sure she can. As long as her name is never mentioned in connection with whatever this is."

"Done. Do you want me to send a car? Not a lot of people back on the subway yet."

"I'll figure it out," Sam assured him. "See you then."

More meet and greet, she thought as she disconnected. The feeling in her stomach wasn't trepidation, though, but anticipation. For better or for worse, she was on a case.

Another text came in almost immediately. Terry, who'd sent a link to a short article from the *Daily News* with the title "Hell Freezes Over." Same mix of speculation and secondhand observation as the other article. Still no mention of dry ice as the weapon but getting dangerously close to the truth. Terry had also added a mix of emojis and a cryptic message:

Have fun and stay out of the spotlight

Despite herself, Sam smiled.

Chapter 6

Manhattan South Homicide Squad made its home in Gramercy Park, a gentrified part of town with several historic apartment buildings and a private park. Sam decided in favor of the subway and against trying to transfer. The F train put her on Sixth Avenue and Twenty-Third Street. An easy walk.

During the crosstown stroll, she stopped to peer through the gate to Gramercy Park, accessible only to residents with keys. The locked bit of greenery reminded her of a *Twilight Zone* episode about people who won the last available plot of land in America and barricaded themselves inside a wire fence to keep out the rest of the world.

She patted her pocket for the piece of paper she'd brought with her. Sam made lists like she took notes, with pen and paper. The exercise served to help her lay out elements of the case at hand. She usually had more information, but she thought the practice could prove useful even this early in the game.

This list took the form of an outline predicated on certain conditions. If A were true, B might follow. If A were not true, something else (C) might follow instead. At some point, conditional conclusions would be proposed. Not ideal but she needed something to work with.

First, she wrote:

I. If Manhattan and Queens homicides are related
  a. The victims are connected to each other by:
    1. Family

2. Friends
3. Background (education, hometown)
4. Employment
5. Shared interests or hobbies (true crime)

The killer would know the victims through the same sorts of interactions that characterized the victims' relationships to each other. She might not have enough information to establish intent, but she could set some parameters. The "why" behind the killings might be traced directly to how the murderer chose the victims. She began with the widely accepted theories as to why people kill.

b. The possible motive is:
1. Desire (love/lust)
2. Greed (envy or material gain)
3. Revenge (punishment or delivery of justice)
4. Ritual
5. Control
6. Thrill-seeking
7. Power-seeking
8. Attention-seeking
9. Self-defense

Scratch self-defense. These murders were too brutal. Revenge, control, a need for power or thrills: these were some of the animating forces behind the murders.

She started a second outline to address the possibility that the Manhattan and Queens murders weren't related. The paper immediately went into the trashcan. The only explanation that two such idiosyncratic murders could be unrelated had to do with a copycat or the unlikelihood that two criminal enterprises with two different motives sent two different enforcers to use the same method on a priest and an actor. Not impossible but not likely.

Therefore, she decided to assume the killings were connected. The podcast was a place to start.

Sam entered the nondescript beige building on East Twenty-Third and rode the elevator to a floor that looked like something out of every TV cop show she'd ever seen, only a little smaller. Desks had been separated and fitted with partitions. A whiteboard stood in one corner. It was clear the fluorescent lighting and dropped ceilings hadn't changed for decades, and the worn floor likely dated back to the nineteen forties. Two offices with doors and windows sat behind the workspaces, along with a separate enclosure with a horizontal window that was likely used for interviews and interrogations. A utilitarian room to one side probably served as a meeting place.

The space came across both as a time capsule and a set piece, although the computers looked up to date and the chairs ergonomically correct. The short entryway featured a stunning painting representing an idealized version of New York.

Times had changed in other ways. A more diverse workforce. More women, including the one who occupied the captain's office.

Zielinski jumped up from his desk. "Lopez is doing a lunch run," he said to explain the empty chair next to his. "She said she needed to stretch her legs. I get it, seeing as she's been at it all morning."

Sam nodded in sympathy. A great deal of detective work was what used to be paperwork and was now online research. Same stiff neck, sore back, and tired eyes. Hours spent reviewing and comparing, searching for the details that might make or break a case. The non-glamorous stuff television rarely shows. Necessary drudge work. Sam had to admit she enjoyed the eureka moments when clues jumped off the screen or patterns suggested themselves.

"Let me have you meet a couple of people," Zielinski suggested. He then spent the next five minutes introducing her to the detectives like a proud brother. She received fist bumps and a generally warm reception, especially when he mentioned she'd been his brother's partner. He'd probably filled them in on a portion of her exploits in Nashville and in Pickett County. She caught the assessing gazes, taking in her height, her barely tamed mass of curly mahogany hair, her wideset eyes. She wondered if they thought she looked like someone who caught serial killers or like she was impersonating someone who did. She got that a lot.

Zielinski popped his head into his CO's office. Marsha Platt was a slender Black woman in her early fifties with graying hair. By way of a greeting, she tipped her head.

"Sam Tate, detective, sheriff, lieutenant, and catcher of serial killers." Her expression tempered her words, as did a slight gleam in her light eyes. "Good to meet you. How are you finding New York?"

"Busy," Sam answered. "Which is a good thing, isn't it?"

"It's a good thing for the city. Tourism is up, but so are homicides. This situation in particular has all the makings of a major PR nightmare. Dry ice, a dead bartender/actor in our area and now a priest in Queens plus a true crime podcast." She pressed a hand to her head. "Anyway, glad for the assist." She turned her gaze to her screen, signaling an end to the meeting.

"She's got a lot on her plate," Sam observed.

"She does," Zielinski agreed. "Hey, Lopez is back with the grub. Excellent. I grabbed the small conference room for half an hour since this'll be a work lunch."

They headed to the larger room. It was surprisingly accommodating, with six chairs, a plain table, and plenty of outlets. Sam spotted a small camera tucked in the corner of the ceiling.

Lopez dumped the food on the table. "Here you go. Iced coffee, iced tea, and your choice of ham and cheese on rye or toasted cheese with tomato. Seemed safe unless you're lactose intolerant or gluten-free or something."

"I'll eat anything," Sam replied. She ended up with a satisfactory ham and cheese and an iced tea.

Lopez pushed a thick folder to Sam.

"These are crime scene photos, along with the ME's report on the Paulson death. Carlisle is pushing for an expedited autopsy on his guy."

Sam had seen plenty of images during her time as a homicide detective. This was different. No blood at all but nonetheless horrific. The victim, Grant Paulson, was slumped against a small refrigerator behind what she assumed was the bar. Possibly rangy in real life, he looked curiously puffed out. His skin was blotchy, mostly gray except around the mouth, which was bright red. Remnants of ice crystals were visible around the lips and tongue.

"How'd the killer get the dry ice down?" Sam asked.

"The ME thinks a funnel was forced into the mouth; he saw evidence of bruising in the back of the throat," Lopez said. "The dry ice was probably in small chunks. There are a couple of techniques to force someone to swallow, none of them pleasant."

"Please tell me he wasn't conscious."

"Not sure. He'd been injected with a fast-acting paralytic but not much remained in the bloodstream. He might have been awake but unable to move."

"That's brutal." Sam shook her head. "Do you have a TOD?"

"The 'when' is interesting," Zielinski said. "ME thinks death took place within two hours of the body's discovery. The bar closes at two a.m., the cleaning crew comes in at three thirty or so. That's a tight timeline. The place was clean as a whistle, which would indicate either experience or preparation. Oh, the service door in back was unlocked, so there's your ingress."

"So, the 'where' is onsite," Sam said. "That's a lot of work, what with getting a significant amount of dry ice into the place and down the victim's throat before tidying up."

"We could be looking at a professional team," Lopez said. "Mob or cartel. They have a fondness for message killings. Maybe related to drugs or a gambling debt." Her smile was grim. "That could describe a bartender or a priest, I'm sorry to say. Nobody's perfect."

"Except we haven't found anything that ties our dead bartender to drugs or gambling," Zielinski said. "He didn't even drink. His interests were limited to his acting, his cycling, his partner—"

"And his favorite weekly podcast," Sam said.

"What do we know about the show?" Zielinski asked.

"I haven't had time to check it out," Lopez replied.

"I did a little research." Sam pulled out her notepad, then looked up to see two pairs of narrowed eyes. "Ron, you asked for my help. This is how I help."

Zielinski made a gesture indicating she continue.

"The show averages more than twelve thousand downloads per episode, which gets them into the top five percent of podcasts. Reviewers like the show's fact-based authenticity. The hosts add a lot of credibility. Tom Levy has a master's degree in journalism from Northwestern. He spent ten years as a crime reporter for the *Chicago Tribune* and another ten at the *Times*, where he was promoted to metro editor. He then took a gig as a special correspondent for CNN. Somewhere along the line, he managed to write a best-selling true crime book about the kidnapping and murder of his two-year-old son back in 1997. And no, they never caught the perpetrators."

"A cold case that's personal," Lopez noted.

"Yep. Then there's Tasha Wright, graduate of John Jay College of Criminal Justice. Former Bronx detective with an enviable close rate. A hopped-up suspect nearly took her out while she was on stakeout. She recovered, then transferred to Manhattan Cold Case Squad. She took retirement a couple of years ago. Either of you know her?"

"Only by reputation," Zielinski said.

Sam continued. "The show boasts an ever-expanding fan base. They must be making money, too. They record in a midtown studio, complete with their own audio engineer."

"NYPD has a podcast that covers similar ground," Lopez said. "Hard to believe they can each pull enough listeners."

"The appetite for true crime seems bottomless," Sam said.

"I think it's time we meet these podcast hosts, Levy and Wright," Zielinski said. "I'll ask Carlisle. Or Lopez and I can go. You want to come along, Sam?"

"Sure," Sam said. "Sounds interesting."

"Ask Carlisle and his new partner to go," Lopez replied. "I have plenty to do."

Zielinski shrugged, more for Sam's benefit than anything else. "I'll set that up for late afternoon and text you the details," he said. "Let me walk you out, Sam."

"Sorry about Lopez," he said at the elevator. "She's aggravated about something today."

"You don't think she has a problem with me, do you?"

"With Lopez, it could be anything," he replied.

A response that didn't answer Sam's question.

Chapter 7

"Good afternoon, true crime fans. You're listening to *Deep Freeze* with your hosts, Tom Levy and Tasha Wright. Today, we're going to focus on a case we named 'Last Call.' Four young women who frequented the same Upper East Side bar went missing in 1982 in the space of two months. They had no connection to one another except their affection for The Bar, as it was cleverly called. What happened to them? Were they kidnapped, killed, or something else? We'll go over what we know."

Wright took over. "Later in the program, we'll review your terrific investigative contributions on the ongoing hunt for the killer of little Kyle Jordan. Today would have been his twenty-first birthday. Hang tight, we'll be right back."

Levy sat back and nodded to the engineer, who punched them out for a sponsor acknowledgement (they didn't use the word "commercial") and a prerecorded segment. Wright pulled off her headphones and grabbed her tea.

"Throat still bothering you?" Levy asked solicitously.

"Always," she responded in her gravelly voice. She touched her slender neck almost absently.

About a dozen years earlier, Wright had been strangled nearly to death. The suspect, a large man under the influence of various amphetamines, had so severely bruised her windpipe she couldn't talk for a month. The attack prompted her move from Homicide to the Cold Case Squad. Wright liked to blame her vocal condition on the incident, but Levy knew years of cigarettes had contributed more than a little to her uneven rasp.

The listeners liked the contrast between the crackle of Wright's voice and the sonorous smoothness of Levy's. She was the prickly one, he the calm antidote. Or so everyone thought. Levy's own burden, his grief, guilt, and fury over his son's death may have surpassed her regrets over the many she left behind.

"Drink up," he said. "Our guests have arrived."

Wright smoothed her chestnut hair. "How do I look?" she asked with an impish grin.

Levy chuckled. Tasha Wright at fifty was still stunning. She was also funny, smart, irreverent, and well-liked by her former colleagues. The fans were divided between those who wanted her and those who wanted to be a version of her.

The alcove outside the studio served as a waiting room. Those expecting to be interviewed usually took a seat. Today's three visitors had crammed into the control room. Levy contained his irritation. These were NYPD detectives. The goal was to be cooperative, especially since the reason for their appearance was certainly tied to a case and possibly material he and Wright could use.

He unfolded his lanky frame from the chair and took a moment to work the kinks out of his neck. "Let's go meet our guests," he said.

Two of them were identifiable as NYPD. The man was objectively good-looking, his one-day scruff no doubt a turn-on for some. Tasha's warm smile when she spotted him suggested she either knew him, or she wanted to. The tallish woman was all business in a plain suit and an all-purpose frown. Behind that tightly controlled veneer, she seemed irritated, even uncomfortable.

The third visitor didn't wear an NYPD shield. Yet she looked familiar to Levy. Reporter? Well-known personality? Local expert? Didn't she resemble the actress who played a detective on a female buddy cop show his wife had liked to watch? Cagney and Lacey? Or the much more recent one with the doctor and the detective. That was it.

When she removed her sunglasses, he realized the woman didn't resemble anyone else he'd ever seen. Her eyes glittered like rare gemstones. No, that wasn't it, more like the new green of spring leaves.

Pull it together, Levy, he ordered himself. The truth was he wasn't all that interested. He missed Emmy, missed his family, missed his old life. All the recognition in the world wouldn't change that pain, and neither would a visitor with an arresting face.

His equilibrium restored, Levy pasted on a smile and pushed through the door.

"Welcome, everyone. We're always happy to see our NYPD friends. You've obviously met our audio engineer and all-around tech guru, Ravi Patel."

The curly-haired young man at the console sprang out of his chair. "I'm going to clear out now," he announced. "I'll be back in, what, half an hour?"

"That'll work," Levy replied. "It's still a little crowded in here, folks. Do you mind if we move next door to our little green room before we continue?" He exited the studio and pushed open an adjacent door to a well-appointed space containing a small refrigerator, a high-end coffee maker, a couch, and several lounge chairs.

"I'm Tom Levy," he continued, ever the affable host. "This is my partner in crime, so to speak, Tasha Wright."

"Detective Dan Carlisle, Queens North Homicide. Nice to meet you, Mr. Levy. I certainly recognize Tasha Wright. Meet Detective Chloe Nichols."

"Queens North Homicide," Wright repeated. She made a point of bending down to read the badge hanging on Carlisle's belt, then straightened. "What are you doing over here, Detectives?" she asked, directing her question at Carlisle.

Levy noticed her voice had taken on a smokey, even sultry quality. The stern-faced detective scowled at her partner; he ignored her.

It was she who answered. "We are pursuing leads on a recent homicide that might be related to one that took place in Manhattan."

Levy turned to the woman who stood quietly while her remarkable eyes moved around the room.

"I'm sorry, I didn't catch your name."

"Sam is fine."

"Are you also from Queens?"

"Sam has been invited to observe," Carlisle jumped in. "She's a homicide investigator."

Levy caught Wright's quizzical expression. She must have felt it, too, that niggling at the edges of the mind, some salient fact struggling to make its way out of the archives and into the light.

"Sit down, everyone, please," Wright said. Everyone did, except the woman named Sam, who chose to lean against the wall.

"Nice setup," Carlisle observed. "Not exactly like recording from your living room."

Levy laughed. "We started that way; then things took off. We're here three or four days a week now. Mondays and Wednesdays, we prerecord segments or promos. Thursdays, we livestream. The other days, we meet with our researchers and develop content."

"About your homicides," Wright prompted, "what exactly makes them related?"

Carlisle, ever the smooth one, focused all his charm on Levy's colleague. "Unfortunately, we can't discuss much at this time, Ms. Wright. What we can tell you is that according to people who knew them, the victims were fans of your show."

"Along with thousands of others from around the tri-state area and beyond," Wright replied. "Doesn't really help us help you, Detective Carlisle, assuming that's why you're here." She softened her blunt response with a pretty smile.

Good girl, Levy thought.

"Is there a type that listens to true crime podcasts?" Nichols queried.

"There are studies that indicate why people listen," Wright said. "Empathy, thrill-seeking, a desire to see justice done. We're new to data mining, but we expect to retain experts to help us target our potential fans. We want to reach any and all interested parties."

"You know who you might want to talk with is Theo Austin, the founder of TCCon," Levy added. "TCCon is an annual convention for lovers of all things true crime. More seasoned providers like CrimeCon and MurderCon have a couple years on them, but TCCon is catching up. It helps that true crime is a growth industry and they have generous benefactors."

"The buzz is strong around their second in-person event," Wright added. "We've been invited to several conferences this year. We're leaning toward TCCon. If anyone can break down the kinds of people who are devoted—or addicted—to true crime, it's Theo."

"Thank you for the information," Nichols said, scratching something down on a pad. "We will follow up."

Out of the corner of his eye, Levy watched Sam push off the wall and make eye contact with the male detective. He nodded, but the other woman had the opposite reaction. She fairly radiated disapproval. Interesting.

"My aunt is a huge fan," Sam began. Levy noticed a soft drawl, more an inflection, that colored her words. "She mentioned she'd love to become what you all call a 'Deep Freeze Detective.' I told her I'd find out what it takes. Sounds like she'd have fun."

Wright laughed. "She'd be working, that's for sure," she said. "We've created several opportunities for people to not only learn about a case but also collaborate if they're inclined to put in the time. For the casual participant, we have message boards, where someone can post a thought. In addition, we have a private 'members only' chat room where serious web sleuths can meet in real time to collaborate on their investigations. Membership is free, but participants have to be accepted."

"Based on what criteria?" Nichols asked.

"They need to demonstrate a sincere interest in justice and a willingness to put in the time," Wright replied. "Participation on the message boards over the course of a month is usually sufficient. It can't hurt to have a DFD make a recommendation."

"Do these people end up meeting each other in real life?" Carlisle asked.

"It's possible they've met previously at conferences. We don't help them identify one another. The chat room, like the message board, is anonymous. Everyone has a username, but no one has to share any other information with each other or with us. Either Tom or I will lurk from time to time, just to make certain no one is bullying, harassing, or threatening anyone else. If there's a problem, Ravi, who is also our tech person, can locate and block the offender. We've had no incidents, by the way. These are people who want to help."

Nichols looked doubtful. "You're saying you don't collect emails or any personal information?"

"We don't," Wright said. "We're not a government agency."

"Out of your thousands of listeners, how many of these citizen detectives would you say you have?" Sam asked.

Levy glanced at Wright. "Maybe twenty or twenty-five who are active," he said.

Nichols didn't try to hide her displeasure. "That's still quite a few people out there playing detective."

"Not playing, Detective, working," Wright said. "And doing a damn good job, by the way. They're not involved with current investigations or visiting active crime scenes. They're providing research services. Some of them have been able to piece together or turn up information that proved useful to the NYPD's Cold Case Squad. In one instance, detectives circled back to an old suspect with new evidence one of our DFDs uncovered and made an arrest. I'd call that a success story."

"You must at least have the names of your Deep Freeze Detectives?" Nichols insisted.

"I imagine we could get that information," Levy replied. "I'll speak to Ravi. But rather than handing you a blanket list, perhaps you can give us more information about your victims. Do you think they were not just listeners but DFDs?"

"When we can share more, we will," Carlisle said. "I'm sure we'll see you again; I suspect we have more to discuss. For now, we don't want to hold you up. We appreciate your time, Mr. Levy, Ms. Wright. We'll show ourselves out."

"Well, that was interesting," Wright said when they'd gone. "I wonder if their hot new homicides have anything to do with our cold cases?"

"Could be," Levy mused. "I'd like to know more about the woman with the precocious aunt."

"Oh, really?" Wright said, raising an eyebrow.

"Not like that, Tasha. But tagalongs aren't exactly SOP, are they?"

"Hard to say. She might have specialized training or experience relevant to their cases. Let me snoop around, see what I can learn. I assume you're on board, Tom?"

"Always."

Chapter 8

Five days into Sam's so-called vacation, she found herself on another police-related field trip, this time to Brooklyn. Rosa had plans: Wednesdays she played canasta.

Carlisle called the night before. "We're divvying up the chores tomorrow. Ron is taking a second run at some of the actor/bartender's acquaintances. Chloe volunteered to do some research on dry ice distributors. You can get a block of the stuff at almost any grocery store these days, but the thinking is our person might be buying in bulk."

"Planning ahead," Sam said. "Makes a perverse kind of sense."

"Lopez and I will talk with this Theo Austin character," he continued. "According to the scheduler, Austin is scouting potential venues for the upcoming TCCon and is briefly available for an interview. We requested a morning meeting. Care to join us?"

Sam hesitated. "Danny, does anyone on the team have a problem with me? I'm not talking about you or Ron."

He chortled. "That pretty much leaves the women. Here's the rundown. Lopez can be a pain, but she's fair-minded. I've known her for years. More to the point, she got behind Ron's move to put you on the investigation. It's probably safe to assume she doesn't have a problem with you."

He took a beat. "What can I say about Nichols? Top of her class at the academy. Decorated for taking down the bad guy. The woman almost broke her back. She pops out of rehab raring to go. Two more citations for bravery. She's dedicated and determined as well as smart. She's also a stickler for procedure. Some cops are like that. I know she can also be a bit grim. I'm sure she's already got a long list of issues with me."

"Well, she has one with me."

"Maybe she doesn't like consultants. Or attractive women. Or famous serial-killer-catching cops from outside NYPD. You can't take it personally. She's young, she's on the fast track, she's likely to have some leftover PTSD from the injury. She can be a little strait-laced, but she'll learn to loosen up. She'll have to if she wants to work with the rest of the squad."

"Because you're all rule breakers?" Sam teased.

"Because homicide work requires flexibility, as you well know."

"I do," Sam said, thinking about the shortcuts she'd taken from time to time. "Changing the subject, what was your takeaway from yesterday's meeting?"

"Levy and Wright are angling for information," Carlisle replied. "They're also playing it a little fast and loose. The idea that they don't collect information on their listeners is bullshit. They probably know what these people ate for dinner."

Sam shivered. She didn't want to think that her aunt might be exposed just for listening. She'd have to have a talk with Rosa.

"I got the same impression," she said.

"Always good to have corroboration. I gotta bounce, Sam. See you tomorrow at nine a.m. Should I buzz by and pick you up?"

"I'll walk. It's close enough." That was untrue, but she didn't want a noticeable NYPD presence in her aunt's neighborhood, at least until she knew which way both the case and her personal investigations were going.

She grabbed an Uber the next morning and had the driver drop her off a block from the precinct. Forest Hills was still lovely, and she enjoyed the stroll. She was surprised to find Margarite Lopez lounging outside the building. Even more startling, the woman waved and smiled. She seemed to have recovered from whatever cramped her mood the other day.

"Hey, Tate!" she called out as Sam approached. "Did you walk over here?"

"It's not far," Sam lied.

Carlisle appeared. He grinned when he saw Lopez and produced a fist bump before turning to Sam with a wave. Good thing her cohorts both managed to get up on the right side of the bed. Unless it was the same bed.

Don't jump to conclusions, she scolded herself. *Maybe they're happy about the nice weather.*

"Okay, ladies, ready to roll?" Carlisle opened the door to his car, a late model Prius in pale gray. "Pile in. We're headed to Industry City."

Sam slid into the back seat. "I thought we were going to Brooklyn."

He smiled at her in the mirror. "We are. Industry City is the name of the private enterprise that operates a huge section of waterfront property in the Sunset Park section. Lots of buildings, lots of space for manufacturing and storage. It even had an active seaport before everything slowed down in the seventies."

"More than thirty years before it came back," Lopez continued. "The owners finally found a couple other mega-investors who had some pretty big ideas about renovating the place as a center for innovation and creativity, along with a maritime hub. Fancy terms for manufacturing, warehousing, and shipping."

"So, the area is revitalized?" Sam asked.

"Bigtime," Carlisle said. "Now you see tech companies, fashion designers, and dance companies operating out of Industry City. There's even a film studio. They've got retail, food, outdoor events. Most important, they have plenty of spaces for rent. Hell, the seaport is back."

"That sounds cool," Sam said. "Smart of Mr. Austin to locate his event there."

"I guess so," Lopez said. "What do we know about him?"

"I did some research," Sam volunteered. She went along with the expected chuckling.

"According to the LinkedIn profile, Austin has a work history that includes a spot of acting, a gig as a corporate flack, some work in the technology sector, and a whole lot of marketing. To give credit where it's due, he's had some success as a concert promoter and special events producer. He even worked in senior management at Comic Con. No picture, though."

"What do we think, ladies?" Carlisle asked. "Twenty-something hipster with a goatee and a fedora? Middle-aged man with a paunch? A silver-haired type in a handmade suit?"

"He's obviously familiar with the world of specialized conferences," Sam said. "Let's hope he can shed some light on the types of people who might show up to a true crime convention."

They arrived at a red brick and sandstone building and entered the light-filled, glassed-in atrium with a view of the harbor and the Manhattan skyline.

Carlisle whistled. “This is a prime piece of property.”

“Yes, it is, although not quite as gritty as I’d like.”

The three detectives turned at the sound of the voice to see a small woman approach. She might have been in her early twenties, her early forties, or anywhere in between. She wore a green hand-painted tunic over black leggings and booties. Her features were delicate, her fair skin enhanced by a smattering of freckles across the bridge of her tiny nose. The pixie-style cut of her copper-colored hair suited her and set off her wide-set cobalt-blue eyes. Peter Pan, right down to the impish grin. Sam half expected her to lift off and fly away, or at least clap her hands to summon a tiny, winged creature.

The woman laughed, no doubt in response to their expressions. The sound echoed off the vaulted space, full-bellied, raucous, loud, and completely at odds with the rest of her. It recalled a crowded bar, not an enchanted forest.

She stopped to wipe a tear from her eye. “Sorry for the surprise,” she said. “I’m Theo Austin, and I’m clearly not what you expected. You’re not the first people to be flabbergasted by my appearance.”

Carlisle recovered first. “I have to admit, I don’t know what I was expecting. I’m Detective Dan Carlisle. To my right is Detective Margarite Lopez. And this is—”

“Sam Tate.” The promoter clapped her hands in delight, like a child listening to her favorite story. “The serial killer-catching county sheriff. My day just keeps getting better.”

“You have a long memory,” Sam said.

"Two years isn't that long, Lieutenant Tate. And you didn't stop with catching killers in rural Tennessee, now did you? On to semi-rural Maryland, where your next case involved pirates, forgeries, and an angry fire-starter turned art dealer. Two cases like that in one year. Some of us don't forget." The blue eyes gleamed. "What brings you to New York?"

"Just visiting and ran into some colleagues. They were kind enough to invite me to tag along."

"How lucky for you." Austin's expression suggested she didn't buy the explanation. "How about we sit down, and you fine officers tell me why you've come looking for me?" She gestured to the padded benches and chair carefully placed at perfect angles to one another.

"I'd invite you up to the event space I'm considering," Austin continued, "but it's not mine to show yet. It will be, though." She perched on the edge of a cushioned bench and tilted her head, a charming sprite ready to summon her magic at a moment's notice.

Lopez leaned forward, hands clasped between her knees. "We have two cases that seem to be connected owing to the manner of death, Ms. Austin. We can't talk specifics. I'm sure you understand. These two homicides shared nothing else in common except an interest in a true crime podcast called *Deep Freeze*."

"Tom Levy and Tasha Wright. Bright people."

"They said the same about you," Lopez said. "They also said you might shed a little insight as to what kinds of people might have an affinity for true crime."

Austin grinned. "Lots of them, which is why I'm in this business. It's an odd premise for an entertainment genre, and yet it's been around in one form or another for centuries. You probably already know that seventy to eighty percent of the people who follow true crime these days, watch the shows, listen to the podcasts, attend the conferences, are women."

"Why the gender gap?" Sam asked.

"There's a growing body of analysis around true crime aficionados and why the genre might appeal especially to women. I'm sure someone is teaching a psychology class on the subject at this very moment. I'll try to summarize the findings. First, women are attracted to the psychology of violent crimes. If they can understand the mind of a killer, the reasoning goes, they can avoid an attack. Not sure that's reasonable, not that it matters." She shrugged.

"Second, they like seeing justice served. And if justice isn't served, if the crimes are unsolved cases, then they are happy to do some controlled sleuthing to help bring closure to the survivors. The Levy-Wright podcast provides a meaningful level of interaction."

"Some of them might be thrill-seekers," Carlisle pointed out.

"Absolutely. That's not a factor to be minimized, either." Austin grew animated as she warmed to her subject. "Both men and women like the adrenaline rush that comes with the chase or the danger. They like to think, 'That could have been me.' They imagine they'd be smarter than the victims or smarter than the criminals. They want to be part of the catch, to solve the case alongside the detectives. Everyone wants to be the hero."

"Except the ones who want to be the villains," Lopez said.

Austin trained her blue gaze on the detective. "Are you looking to find a killer among true crime lovers,

Detective Lopez? Because you're dealing with an enormous group of fans. Even if you limit your search to those who listen to *Deep Freeze*, you're still talking thousands."

"We're trying to put together a profile," Carlisle said. "To understand the victims as well as the murderer or murderers."

Austin nodded. "I see. True crime attracts its share of people who are drawn to the more gruesome crimes. There's a subgenre of fans, far more men than women in this instance, who celebrate the serial killers and pay little attention to the victims. They have T-shirts with images of Ted Bundy, Jeffrey Dahmer, Jack the Ripper, or John Wayne Gacy. They listen to podcasts and show up at true crime conventions like mine. They also meet on message boards and chat rooms to discuss the best way to kill or maim or torture someone or dispose of the bodies. Their numbers are growing."

She looked pleased, rather than disturbed, as if she were discussing favorite foods or even memorable pranks, not murder.

"Don't get me wrong," she continued. "Killer-worship is not to my taste. But that's part of what's great about the genre. We never lack for people who are fascinated by crime, and we never run out of crimes to fascinate them. Up to now, women have predominated. I aim to change that. The more people you appeal to, the more money you make. Last year, forty percent of our online attendees were men. That's far more than any other show or venue can claim. I don't honestly care if they're wanna-be detectives or wanna-be killers. We have room for all of them."

Austin flung her arms wide and laughed her boisterous laugh. No one else joined in.

Chapter 9

They'd just returned to the precinct when Carlisle's phone went off. He glanced at the text. "I'm being called to a 187. Main branch of the Queens Public Library. Jamaica belongs to Queens South. So why—ah, shit!"

"What?" Lopez asked

"Per 9-1-1, victim appears to have sustained freezer-like burns. Goddamn, not another one."

All three exchanged looks.

"I gotta get back," Lopez said. "Sam? Can you ride with Danny?" She jumped out. Sam took her place in the passenger seat.

"Keep me posted," Lopez yelled as the car sped away.

"Wait, what about Chloe?" Sam asked as she strapped in.

"No time. I'll text her when we get there." Carlisle threw the flashers onto the dashboard and drove like a bat out of hell, alternately muttering, honking, and tromping on the accelerator.

"Alive, please," Sam said, which earned her a side-eye.

"I don't suppose you were yelling at traffic out in Pickett County."

"Nope. We saved our cussing for blinding dust or small critters that crossed the road."

His weak smile did little to ease her nerves.

Carlisle parked in front of a plain structure that reminded Sam of a federal building. Several police vehicles sat helter-skelter on the street next to hastily erected barriers. Uniformed officers guided members of the public out through the library entrance and kept others from coming in.

"This is the central hub for one of the busiest library systems in the country," Carlisle said as they climbed out. "It's got classrooms, auditoriums, an entire new addition for children. It's always busy. This situation is bad."

Pride of place, Sam thought. She wondered if the case was about to get personal for Detective Dan Carlisle.

"Do you want me to hang back and observe?" she asked.

"I want you to bring your experience to bear on the case. Whatever you have to say, within reason, should work just fine."

Sam followed Carlisle to a door just off the main entrance. His credentials got them waved into the lobby where they were greeted by a sturdy sandy-haired woman in slacks, a blazer, and a mask that read NYPD.

"Arlene Garner," she said.

Carlisle made introductions.

"The library is my precinct, but we got a homicide detective from South in almost immediately. Andy Mills. He's upstairs. We also went ahead and called the ME's office. The MLI showed up maybe five minutes ago. Oh, and my CO suggested you'd want to take the lead, what with the, ah, wider implications. We've got no problem with that. And I don't think Detective Mills does, either."

"I thought Mills had retired," Carlisle said.

"Close enough," Garner replied.

Sam couldn't help but wonder if Detective Mills hoped this homicide would tie back to the bartender and the priest, which would potentially make it someone else's problem. Not her concern, she decided. She was here to support Danny.

"What can you tell us about the victim?" she asked.

Garner looked at her phone. "Stephanie Chen, twenty-three, worked in the library's music reference center for about a year. Majored in music, pursuing a graduate degree in Library Science at Queens College. Only child of immigrant parents who run a small grocery store in Flushing. We've got a Cantonese-speaking precinct detective who will head over to notify them."

"Okay," Carlisle said. "Let's head on up."

They took the stairs to a light-filled hallway on the second floor and down to a small room filled with stacks. Two patrolmen were stringing crime scene tape around the area. Two young people stood weeping with their heads pressed together.

Garner nodded in their direction. "Fellow researchers. They're devastated, as you can see. From what we can gather, they went to a staff meeting from four to four forty-five. The victim stayed behind to pull together a request from a branch library for some sheet music. Then those two came back and found her."

"They were only gone forty-five minutes?" Sam exclaimed. She looked at Carlisle; he was thinking the same thing.

"Detective Mills!" Garner waved over a portly, white-haired man in an ill-fitting blue jacket. He yanked on a mask that didn't quite make it to his nose. A cop on the brink of retirement, Sam decided. The eyes, however, suggested this cop was still very present, capable of collecting, sifting through, and assessing information. A seasoned investigator.

"Andy Mills," he introduced himself in a voice as weathered as his face. "Eighty-two days away from retirement and this is the memory I'll probably leave with. How are you, Danny?"

"Remains to be seen," Carlisle said. "This is Sam Tate."

"Have at it, Detectives," Mills said and pointed to a group of stacks.

The body lay in a narrow space between two shelves. A compact man with glasses and abundant sable hair was trying to take pictures while maneuvering in the small space. He spotted the detectives and turned to greet them. A bushy beard fought to escape his mask.

"Detectives, I don't believe we've met," he said in a barely audible voice. "Alan King from the ME's office."

They introduced themselves. "What can you tell us?" Carlisle asked.

"That the assailant chose an unusual method. I suspect you already knew that; otherwise, why would two borough homicide detectives be present? And yes, this has much in common with another scene I processed two days ago. First, I need you two to give this area a wide berth. I have enough problems without any more contamination than is necessary." He waved them back.

While King delivered his clinical findings, Sam looked beyond him to the young woman who lay on the floor. Petite, wearing a cardigan sweater, colorful skirt, tights, and short boots. Inky shoulder-length hair, bangs. Splotchy skin tone devoid of color, much like the images Sam had seen of the bartender. Black and red around the mouth, as if she'd tried to swallow fire. Her jaw was wrenched open, and she was missing a few teeth. She had a burn on her hand.

"From what I can see," King went on, "the tissue inside is consistent with a chemical burn. Her throat is scorched. It's also scraped in parts. I'd need her on a table to do a proper exam, but I'd say something was shoved down there. Maybe dry ice, maybe whatever was used to force down the ice. Her stomach is distended; the lining was probably compromised. The yellow of her eyes indicates liver damage as well."

"Was the victim's jaw broken?" Carlisle asked.

"The temporomandibular or TM joint was disabled and some of the muscles were torn," the investigator answered. "I'd want an autopsy to confirm, but it seems the mouth was pried and held open by a precision tool of some kind. Hers is a very small aperture and the killer may have used a type of funnel."

"That must have been agony," Sam said.

The MLI tilted his head. "I suppose it was, although I can tell you the killer worked with remarkable efficiency."

Efficient but still torture, Sam wanted to object. Instead, she asked, "Are there any differences between this victim and the priest?"

"What do you mean?"

Sam pointed to the body. "Her fingers are discolored, as if she'd been burned. Or she'd gotten frostbitten. Did she fight back? Is it possible she grabbed whatever was pushed into her mouth? Maybe even touched the assailant?"

"Anything's possible." King's smile never reached his eyes. "Perhaps a stray chunk of dry ice dropped onto her hand. My job is to consider all the possibilities."

"Of course," Carlisle interjected. "Why don't we leave you to it? Have you spoken with any witnesses?"

"Not yet. There are two coworkers, both very distraught. Maybe you can work with that."

His tone implied he could not or would not.

"Thank you."

"I trust you'll share any pertinent information you obtain," King called out.

"Naturally."

"He seems nice," Sam said. "Sarcasm intended."

"Cut the guy some slack," Carlisle responded. "Medicolegal investigators are overworked and underappreciated."

"Excuse me, but if you're going to interview my employees, I will need to be present." The calm, firm voice belonged to a slim, dark-skinned woman in gray slacks and a burgundy sweater that matched both her eyeglass frames and her mask. "I'm Dr. Nina Vaughn, head librarian," she continued. "I appreciate the gravity of the situation and the need to extract information. I just want to make sure everything proceeds smoothly."

"I assume they're both adults—" Carlisle began.

"And I'm in charge. We also have a lawyer on staff. Will she be needed?"

"Not at all," Sam said gently. "We understand Stephanie's coworkers have been through a traumatic experience. We simply want to collect background while we're here."

The librarian relaxed. "Thank you for your understanding. This is a hideous occurrence. Let's all go into the small conference room in the back and away from the goings-on."

"I'll join you, if you don't mind." Chloe Nichols stood just behind Vaughn. Her suit was a drab version of navy. She looked even more tightly wound than usual. It occurred to Sam that the woman could appear more approachable if she loosened her hair and thought about adding some color to her wardrobe. Although maybe inaccessible was the goal.

They took their seats around a long table. Vaughn introduced the assistants as Lea Caplan and Oliver Rhodes. Lea was short and buxom, with a glorious crown of curly toffee-colored hair that tumbled down her back. Her large brown eyes periodically filled with tears. The young man was tall and thin, with delicate features and a tidy goatee. His hands fluttered in front of his face like trapped birds. He'd drop them to his side; they'd fly right back up.

They dropped their masks to drink the water and use the Kleenex their employer had kindly provided. Finally, they'd composed themselves sufficiently enough to answer questions.

Carlisle and Nichols took them through the discovery of the body, the frantic dash to the administrative offices on the first floor, the panicked report to Dr. Vaughn and the call to 9-1-1.

"So, you both left to report the incident downstairs," Nichols said. "How long were you gone?"

Caplan's eyes widened. "I ... we ... I guess we stayed down there until the police arrived. Was that a mistake?"

"You made the safest possible choice," Carlisle reassured them. "Did you notice anyone in the hallway either time, someone who didn't belong there?"

"Did we?" Rhodes looked worried. "I can't say. I mean, we have a couple of classrooms on this floor, and everyone seems to wear a hoodie or carry a backpack. Add in the masks and ..." He used his hands to complete the sentence.

"Don't worry about that," Sam said. "I want to focus on Stephanie. How well did you know her? Did you hang out?"

Rhodes perked up. "We were pretty much Zoom buddies for most of last year," he said. "We got close. Every now and then one of us would come in, along with our supervisor, Rita Gupta. She got sick, though, and we didn't start back at the library until this past summer."

"Then we made up for lost time." Caplan giggled. "At least Stephanie did."

"Was she a party girl?" Nichols asked.

"Oh my God; nothing like that. She had graduate school and two jobs. I don't know when she managed to sleep. But she had a great personality. She knew a lot of people and she had a lot of friends. Friends from college, from grad school, from her community; I mean, other first-generation Chinese Americans like her."

"Plus, she was in this Facebook group for music history nerds and some true crime online group connected to a podcast," Rhodes added. "She said she got to play detective."

"Do you remember the name?" Nichols had her notepad out.

Rhodes shrugged. "Something about old cases or maybe cold cases? I didn't pay a whole lot of attention."

Carlisle stood. "You have been very helpful, both of you. Go home, talk to a friend, get some rest. If we need anything further from you, we'll ask Dr. Vaughn to contact you."

Nichols pulled Carlisle back as the rest of the group walked out of the conference room. Sam turned around to find them in a heated exchange. Nichols fumed while Carlisle appeared to toggle between irritation and amusement. After a minute or so, Nichols stormed out, fists clenched. Carlisle returned Sam's quizzical look with a shrug.

"Forget about that," he told her. "I need to fill Garner in and then we can head out."

Sam didn't want to forget. She suspected she was the source of the argument. She'd picked up a negative vibe from Nichols that went beyond a bad day or a lousy disposition. Time to find out what the woman's issues were.

Except Nichols was nowhere to be seen. Sam promised herself she'd take up the matter—whatever the matter was—sooner rather than later. But first, she had a more pressing piece of business to handle.

She located Andy Mills at the room's entrance.

"Done for the day, Detective Tate?" he asked, pulling down his mask.

"Unlikely, Detective Mills. If you don't mind my asking, have you spent your career in Queens?"

"I'm one of those rare birds that moved up without leaving the borough. Only ever worked two places, the 112 and now homicide." His shrewd slate eyes searched her face. "Why do you ask?"

Sam's heart began to race. "I wonder if you might have worked an old case, back in the early nineties. Before my time," she added.

He cocked his head. "You got any more details?"

"You know, now's probably not a good time to talk. Maybe I can take you for coffee or lunch and pick your brain."

"Sure, why not? I'm a sucker for free food." He pulled a card from his pocket. "Call me to set up a date. Make it soon. I don't have a lot of time."

Do any of us? Sam wondered. She gave a two-finger salute and followed Carlisle to the car, clutching the card that might represent a connection to her past.

Chapter 10

The young girl saw the police car before anyone else did. Lights flashing and siren blaring, it entered the wedding hall and exited out to the back where the guests sat in neat rows of white chairs. The vehicle tore down the path the wedding party had just trod moments earlier. A cold vapor rose from the engine. Flames shot out of the tailpipe. As it raced toward the platform, the little girl standing on it struggled to scream, but her voice box froze. No one could call for help. No one could stop the inevitable.

Sam woke drenched in sweat and cursing the subconscious region of her brain that delighted in producing her night terrors. The digital clock near her bed read 5:00 a.m. She'd stayed up past eleven to watch the news. The story was still in its infancy but rapidly taking shape. #DryIceKiller was trending on Twitter. The inevitable spread from local to cable to national news was ahead. No one had mentioned the podcast yet, but Levy and Wright weren't about to let such a prime public relations moment slip by. She suspected they had a smart agent working late into the night to wrangle a spot for them on the morning shows.

She pulled on sweatpants and a shirt and pushed herself out the door and down the narrow steps for a thirty-minute run. She wasn't used to concrete, and she regretted not heading to a park. But she needed to get ready for the onslaught, preferably with a cup of coffee in hand.

The cerulean sky was tinted pink at the horizon. What was the old saying? "Red skies at morning, sailors take warning." No clouds in the sky, but she expected choppy waters.

Her text pinged at 5:45. Zielinski.

Hope you're awake. Whatever you do, don't do anything.

Well, that's cryptic, she thought.

She jumped in and out of the shower, came down in a big sweater and leggings, and poured coffee into the largest mug she could find. She was about to check the rest of her texts when her phone rang.

To her surprise, the call wasn't Ron or even Terry but Bruce Gordy, the Talbot County senior detective under her command.

"Morning, Lieutenant," he said cheerfully. "Figured I'd find you up bright and early. Are you checking to make sure they're spelling your name correctly?"

"What are you talking about, Gordy?"

"The Dry Ice Killer? It's all over the news. Which we get out here on Maryland's Eastern Shore, thanks to something called the internet. What I don't get is how you got yourself in the middle of a possible serial killing spree while on vacation."

"I'm not in the middle of anything. The lead detective is the brother of my partner back in Nashville. We ran into each other, that's all."

"I get the impression it's more than that. Like you're working as some special kind of consultant to the NYPD."

"What? Where did you hear that? I just tagged along on a couple of interviews."

"Check CNN online," Gordy said. "Or MSNBC. Or the early editions of the *Washington Post,* the *Baltimore Sun,* and the *New York Post* for starters. I bet

Shana has already started compiling links to various articles."

Shana Pierce was Talbot County Sheriff Department's internet guru and tech specialist.

"Gordy, I need to get on top of this. Does Sheriff Reed know yet?"

"He will soon enough, Lieutenant."

"All right. I'm going to try and clear up this misunderstanding. Tell him I'll call him later today, will you?"

"Will do. And good luck."

Sam disconnected and logged into her work email to find it filled with requests from various outlets. She moved over to text messages. Nothing yet from reporters or producers but texts from Ron, Danny Carlisle, and Sheriff Tanner Reed, her boss.

The phone rang.

"Ron," Sam said.

"This thing has blown up," he started in. "The coverage is every bit as sensationalized as you might think. Lots of details out there that shouldn't be. I would love to know how that happened. I've heard from my captain. The chief of detectives has called to offer help."

"What kind of help?"

"For now, they will step out front of any public disclosures. He and the mayor's office want to, as they put it, 'take back the narrative.' Make it about seeking the public's help while reassuring them they're not about to be fast-frozen by some psycho. We still get to actually investigate the case, but I think we're on a timeline."

"And by 'we' you mean ..." Sam let the sentence trail off.

Zielinski exhaled. "Here's the thing, Sam. NYPD hires consultants all the time. Forensic experts, historians, psychologists, former CIA and FBI agents, hell, even mentalists. As far as I'm concerned, you have a skill set, not to mention recent experience on strange cases."

"There's a 'but' coming."

"Your profile is distinctive. Your name is distinctive. You're distinctive. Theo Austin had no problem recognizing you. Tom Levy and Tasha Wright have probably worked out who you are by now. The detectives you met at the library weren't born yesterday. Someone within the department may be leaking information to the press. Put it all together and—"

"I'm a distraction."

"You're a series of distracting questions. Did the NYPD bring in a flashy outsider for publicity? Why would a city department need a county cop's help? Don't they have people in the department with the required investigative experience? If not, why not? Will they call in the FBI and when? And on and on."

She groaned. "Ron, I'm sorry if I've caused any issues for you and the rest of the team."

"It's nothing we can't handle, okay?" Ron went on. "More of a PR problem than anything else. The chief is calling a press conference this morning at seven. Early as hell, but rumor has it Levy and Wright got themselves booked on one of the morning shows by claiming to be assisting us. If and only if your name comes up, the chief will say that you happened to be in town for a few days and were invited to share insights when and if needed. Nothing unusual, done all the time. That should end speculation over your role. The press still has plenty to chew on, especially since we have a killer who might be escalating and no clue as to who he, she, or they may be."

Sam rubbed the spot between her eyes, her automatic response to stress. She took a deep breath in and slowly released it. She'd make sure to get in a yoga practice today. At least she'd have time for it.

"I understand, Ron, and I appreciate your honesty. I enjoyed meeting everyone. Good luck."

"Hold on, Tate. You're not getting off that easily. Unless you want to. We have to temporarily reduce your visibility, yes. But I'm not about to turn away the services of someone with your experience with ritual killers. Again, your call."

"What'd you have in mind?" Sam asked, ignoring the voice that warned her to walk away.

"How'd you like to become a Deep Freeze Detective?"

Chapter 11

Sam had the day off from the case she wasn't supposed to be working. Zielinski was coordinating with his tech people to get her set up in the Deep Freeze chat room. He promised they would come up with a plausible explanation for her apparent absence on the message boards before being invited onto the chat. Sam was happy to leave the creative backstories to the NYPD.

"How'd you like to do something with me today?" she asked Rosa over toast and jam, a welcome reprieve from the heavy breakfasts her aunt usually served. Predictably, the older woman had grumbled about not being allowed to properly feed people in her own house. Sam stood her ground.

"I'll have to clear my schedule," Rosa replied.

"Of course. I should have—"

"I'm teasing you, *tesora*. I have all the time in the world for you." She gave Sam an appraising look. "No police work?"

"I'm all yours, Aunt Rosa."

"Good. So, I wanna go by St. Joseph's, look for myself, you know? You got some pull, right? In case we're not supposed to go in. Then we can walk over to Ovelia for lunch. You eat Greek, right? Oh, and we need to stop first at the pet store on Broadway."

Sam stifled a protest. She hadn't considered a visit to a former crime scene as part of the day's itinerary. Or a pet store, for that matter. Instead, she said, "It sounds fine, Rosa. I just have to call my boss in Maryland. That won't take long."

"We're leaving at nine," Rosa announced and mounted the stairs humming.

Sam refilled her coffee mug. She needed to call Tanner Reed to apologize for not reaching out yesterday. She could reassure him that while she was a little preoccupied, she had everything under control. With any luck, he wouldn't be in, and she could leave a voice mail.

He answered on the first ring. "Lieutenant Tate, good morning."

"Sheriff." In the pause that followed, she cleared her throat. "I, um, thought I'd check in, see how things are going."

"Since you left the department in Detective Gordy's capable hands while you went on *vacation*"—he emphasized the word—"then you know we're fine back home. It's quiet, unlike what you've got going on in New York. Which is what, exactly?"

Sam gave him a thumbnail of the events of the past five days. She finished with assurances that she was no longer involved.

Tanner chuckled. "Sounds as if the NYPD has an issue with accepting outside help, even if they request it."

"To be fair, sir, they seem more accommodating than certain other elements."

"Ah, yes. The politicians, the press, and the public. That's a lot of pressure to land on the department. And on you." Tanner lowered his voice. "Sam, you don't have to take the heat for the NYPD. I may be out of line, but I have the impression your visit to New York isn't a casual one. Whatever it is you need to take care of should be your priority. You might also want to take some quality time for yourself away from police work. Okay?"

It occurred to Sam that Reed was a better investigator than she'd realized. Or maybe, like any veteran cop, he had solid instincts he trusted. He also cared about the people in his department.

"Thanks, Sheriff," she said. "I'll be smart."

"I expect no less," Tanner said and disconnected.

She stared at the phone, trying to decide if she felt better or worse. Her boss was nothing but supportive. Yet she had to wonder if she'd messed up again. Maybe it was time to move on. She'd worked to make a home for herself on Maryland's Eastern Shore. She'd done the same during her three years in Pickett County, Tennessee, and her nine in Nashville before that. Yet she remained a visitor assigned to live among a group of people, ordered to assimilate as best as possible until she was moved by whatever impulse or event served as her overlord.

Dr. Putnam, her therapist, would call that a classic case of alienation, not that they'd spoken for two months. She wondered if her reticence to schedule a session was related to her strained relationship with Terry. He'd recommended Putnam. Or maybe Sam didn't want to be reminded that she had a problem with connection, never mind commitment.

At least she'd driven herself to New York to visit the sister of her dead father, walk the old neighborhood, and seek out answers that might help bring some sort of resolution, or at least an end to the nightmares. That had to count for something, didn't it?

She couldn't answer that, so she ran upstairs to change into jeans and a sweater. She tied her hair back and put on her Ray-Bans. Not exactly incognito but less likely to attract attention.

On the way out of her room, she reached for a shelf in the closet to touch her gun box. As an active-duty officer, she was allowed to transport firearms across state lines. Nonetheless, she'd debated about bringing her service revolver. In the end, she felt better bringing it along than leaving it in her rental cottage.

Rosa came down the stairs dressed in plain black slacks, sensible shoes, and a red cardigan. She'd added a voluminous multicolored scarf that threatened to envelop her completely.

"Let's go," she said. "I want to be at the pet store right when it opens. Make sure you take your mask."

The store in question was on Thirtieth Avenue. They walked down a street that had not quite returned to normal. Stores were open but many establishments requested or required masks. Pawsitively Purrfect, was one of those.

They pushed inside to a retail store with neatly arranged supplies appropriate to the care and feeding of dogs, cats, birds, and certain small rodents. What Sam didn't see were any pets.

A balding middle-aged man with glasses set precariously on his head and a mask with feline and canine paw prints waved at Rosa as she entered.

"Hi, Vincent," Rosa said. "This is my niece, Sam. To Sam she said, "Vincent owns the store and Melinda behind the counter is his daughter."

"Sam, nice to meet you," Vincent said with a grin. "Rosa, I'm sure you're here to see your friend. Maybe you can get her to rouse herself today."

"Come on, Vincent, she deserves to rest."

Melinda left the counter and led the two women to a door in the far corner of the store which opened onto a supply room.

The "friend" turned out to be a hefty, golden-orange tabby with dark brown stripes and an M-shaped mark on her forehead. She was reclining in a large fleece-lined bed within a fenced-in section while five tiny and energetic kittens tumbled around her.

Rosa carefully stepped over the low wire fence and eased herself down to the floor. Melinda and Sam squatted on either side of her.

"The mama is Cinnamon," Rosa explained. "Vincent found her after she'd gotten herself in trouble. He's pretty attached to her, so odds are she'll stay. The kittens will all need new homes in a couple of weeks, right?" She looked at Melinda, who scooped up a couple of the little ones and handed them out like gifts.

"Right," the young woman responded. "We're weaning them right now. At eight weeks, they'll be ready for their forever homes."

"Are you thinking of getting a kitten, Aunt Rosa?" Sam asked.

"Don't be silly," her aunt replied. She struggled to her feet, still holding a tiny animal, and missed the smile Sam directed at Melinda.

After surrendering the kittens, Sam and Rosa left the store and strolled down Broadway, their pace leisurely. It was another fine fall day, with temperatures promising to climb to seventy again. Rosa chatted away, and Sam was content to listen.

"Vincent's store made it through the pandemic, mainly because everyone bought pets. Now everyone wants to get rid of their pets, and he's thinking of getting into the rescue business. I told him it was a losing proposition. Stick with what you know. Like restaurants. You remember Sandford? Good basic food since the Depression. Your father loved that place. They're still there. But Vaccaro's Bakery on Steinway? Gone. Closed even before the virus showed up. Heard they'd relocated to Jersey."

"Vaccaro's, the Cake King of Queens," Sam exclaimed. "I can't believe I remembered that."

"At least the churches have survived," Rosa observed. "Guess people have to pray."

They arrived at St. Joseph's to discover, as Sam expected, nothing left to indicate a vicious crime had taken place just days earlier.

Rosa hid her disappointment with a shrug. "Might as well go in."

"Hold on, Rosa. I wanted to ask you why my mother sometimes came here instead of Our Lady of Mount Carmel."

"I think your mother needed to be alone with her sorrow," Rosa said.

"I know she was unhappy. Was it her marriage? My father? Me and my brother?"

"Absolutely not. She adored you all." Rosa searched her niece's face. "You really don't know." She sighed, a deep exhale that contained decades of pain. Then she pointed to a bench across from the church. "Let's sit down there. We can go inside St. Joe's afterwards."

She settled herself onto the seat and Sam joined her.

"I don't know why they never told you," Rosa continued. "Maybe your mother thought you were too young, and maybe your aunt thought you already knew."

"Knew what?"

"You had another brother who died before you were born, *cara*. He would have been, let's see, eight years older than you."

Sam stared at her aunt, too stunned to comment.

"His name was Michael," Rosa said. "Everyone called him Mickey. He had red hair, blue-green eyes, and freckles. One hundred percent looked like your mother and her side of the family. But his personality was all your dad. Strong-willed, charming, and prone to mischief. He arrived four years after Stefan and trust me, your parents were thrilled. They'd worried about providing their oldest with a sibling the whole time."

"What happened to him?" Sam asked.

"He was run over by a delivery truck when he was five. Let himself out of the yard and popped into the street and boom! Died on the spot. It was an accident plain and simple, but your mother blamed herself. She mourned the boy for a long time. I mean, we all did. But for your mom, it was like the spirit drained out of her. Nothing could bring her all the way back. Until you were born."

"But she kept coming here to grieve."

Rosa patted Sam's hand. "To pray, dear heart. To try to make sense of it all. It didn't change how she felt about you."

Sam didn't reply.

"I'm gonna head in, light a candle for Johnny and your father. I'll light one for Mickey as well. Do you want to come in?" She touched Sam's shoulder. "Or maybe stay. I'll be right back."

Sam watched her aunt cross the street and enter the church. Rosa would say prayers for the dead while Sam would be left to consider how much she didn't know about the two women who raised her.

She was alerted to a text from Ron.

It's a go. We'll set you up tomorrow.

Chapter 12

[Transcript of chat 10/15/21, 12pm EDT https://deepfreeze/dfd/]

@workingmom: Hey, everyone, thanks for making me this week's moderator

@deepdiver: cheerleader, you mean

@workingmom: ha ha. Anyway, say hi to our newest DFD, @countyhunter

@renaissancewoman: welcome

@truthsleuth: welcome aboard

@puzzlemaven: clever name

@teacherpreacher: hey

@justicewarrior: Sorry, but where did you come from?

@seenitall: I don't remember you from the message board

@notmydayjob: How did you cut to the front?

@deepdiver: Don't DFDs have to log time on the message boards?

@workingmom: Take your hands off your keyboards, people. Let countyhunter answer

@countyhunter: I was on for two months under the name @scutwork. Someone else hacked the name.

@truthsleuth: Chaos ensued

@teacherpreacher: I think I remember @scutwork

@justicewarrior: So now you're countyhunter

@notmydayjob: scutwork to countyhunter. A promotion?

@workingmom: It doesn't matter. Glad to have you aboard

@countyhunter: Thanks. Lots of names to remember

@deepdiver: You'll get to know us

@cloakndagger: for better and for worse

@notmydayjob: Everyone's a comic

@workingmom: How'd you find us?

@countyhunter: Longtime podcast fan, first live chat

@workingmom: Don't worry, we don't judge

@notmydayjob: says you

@puzzlemaven: Chat is more personal

@teacherpreacher: more social

@renaissancewoman: more collaborative

@seenitall: DFDs are more focused on the work

@workingmom: We take our work seriously

@notmydayjob: absolutely

@countyhunter: got it

@deepdiver: Speaking of work, where are we on the Kyle Jordan case?

@puzzlemaven: Anyone know why they never questioned his kindergarten teacher?

@justicewarrior: They did, but only about Kyle's whereabouts that day

@workingmom: Who thought of asking about the boy's inhaler?

@deepdiver: That was @teacherpreacher. Nice work, by the way

@teacherpreacher: Thanks. The devil is in the details

@cloakndagger: always

@justicewarrior: Amen to that!

@seenitall: Let's get back to the forensic evidence collected

@notmydayjob: again?

@seenitall: Excuse me if I respect the process

@renaissancewoman: as you should

@workingmom: We already looked at what Nassau County police collected off the victim

@teacherpreacher: which wasn't very much

@notmydayjob: and didn't match any markers in a national database

@seenitall: That's because the wrong parameters were used

@puzzlemaven: Here we go

@countyhunter: What's going on?

@deepdiver: You have to excuse @seenitall, who maybe could change their name to @knowitall

@seenitall: says the rank amateur

@puzzlemaven: Come on. We're all amateurs on here

@teacherpreacher: Perhaps @seenitall has an expertise they can apply to the case

@notmydayjob: By all means, please share

@renaissancewoman: Let's not tear each other down

@brains&beauty: Hello, we have more pressing issues to discuss

@workingmom: What do you mean?

@brains&beauty: Why are we talking about this cold case today?

@justicewarrior: That's pretty much the point of what we do here

@brains&beauty: Normally, but we have a hot case to worry about

@truthsleuth: What are you talking about?

@notmydayjob: Bet she means the Dry Ice Killer

@justicewarrior: not our concern

@cloakndagger: I agree

@brains&beauty: What if the killer is targeting us?

@justicewarrior: Excuse me?

@seenitall: That's an interesting premise

@renaissancewoman: You can't be serious

@puzzlemaven: What are you talking about?

@notmydayjob: That's all we need

@brains&beauty: Ask yourself: Why were Levy and Wright making the rounds of the talk shows after the latest murder?

@justicewarrior: They were looking for publicity?

@workingmom: They mentioned a visit from NYPD on the latest podcast

@justicewarrior: So what? They said they couldn't offer much.

@brains&beauty: Not sure that's true

@truthsleuth: Were the names of the victims released?

@workingmom: Yeah, they were. Hang on. Grant Paulson, Father Thomas Clemons, Stephanie Chen

@truthsleuth: Any details about them?

@workingmom: Bartender, priest, research librarian and something about where they worked. One in Manhattan, two in Queens

@truthsleuth: Nothing about their hobbies or interests?

@renaissancewoman: We're really getting off topic

@justicewarrior: Where are you going with this?

@notmydayjob: I'd say we're going off the rails

@truthsleuth: Why were three random people murdered in such a weird way?

@cloakndagger: Seems like an unpleasant way to die

@truthsleuth: Seems like a message

@seenitall: almost as if they weren't random, you mean

@justicewarrior: shared hobbies or traits?

@workingmom: I'd say they were all cold-hearted, but a priest isn't likely to be

@brains&beauty: You're right. A priest is in the business of saving souls

@notmydayjob: We had a member named @soulsaver

@workingmom: You think that was the priest who got murdered?

@deepdiver: Shit!

@renaissancewoman: That can't be right

@workingmom: @soulsaver isn't on today

@justicewarrior: Maybe he, she, or they are sick

@seenitall: or sick of us

@puzzlemaven: Is @bythebook on today?

@cloakndagger: That's the one who knows all the tricks and pitfalls of internet searching

@brains&beauty: almost like a research librarian

@truthsleuth: I knew it!

@brains&beauty: Now you're starting to put it together

@workingmom: @bythebook isn't on the chat. First time that I can remember

@teacherpreacher: Come on. There are plenty of book lovers and @soulsaver could be a therapist

@notmydayjob: or a cult leader

@renaissancewoman: I'm not sure we should be discussing this

@teacherpreacher: Fewer than half the DFDs chat regularly. It's a major time suck. I'm often tempted to skip a day

@brains&beauty: But you don't. And we all still post on the message board. I haven't seen anything from @soulsaver or @bythebook over the last few days, have you?

@renaissancewoman: I don't think we can jump to any conclusions

@workingmom: When's the last time we heard from @actingcyclist?

@cloakndagger: Why?

@workingmom: I read the first victim, Grant Paulson, was an actor and cyclist

@deepdiver: shit @countyhunter: Hard to believe these three were picked out of thousands who listen to true crime podcasts

@puzzlemaven: no lack for imagination on this chat

@justicewarrior: I agree with @countyhunter.

@brains&beauty: You have ppl who like true crime. Some of them want to solve cold cases. A smaller group listens to Deep Freeze. BTW, the victims were killed with dry ice. Doesn't anyone else see the connection?

@justicewarrior: coincidence

@truthsleuth: It feels like more than coincidence to me

@teacherpreacher: Why target us? Is it related to the Kyle Jordan case? Are we getting too close?

@brains&beauty: Maybe it's something else

@puzzlemaven: What did any of us do to provoke a killer?

@notmydayjob: How hard is it to stir up a psycho?

@seenitall: You think this is a crazy person?

@deepdiver: You think it's not?

@brains&beauty: The killings are methodical. They suggest a certain skill set

@seenitall: I agree with you

@truthsleuth: a certain mindset

@cloakndagger: Are we sure these victims were members of our chat?

@workingmom: We need to discuss with Tom and Tasha. They have access to our real emails, don't they?

@notmydayjob: If they don't, it's pretty easy to get them

@renaissancewoman: It is?

@truthsleuth: It's not that hard if you have the tech skills

@brains&beauty: And if you're already online chatting with us

@deepdiver: shit!

@countyhunter: You think the killer is online right now?

@justicewarrior: That's over the top

@renaissancewoman: What if it's true?

@teacherpreacher: Sorry, folks, I'm out of here

@puzzlemaven: same here

@seenitall: You're all signing off?

@notmydayjob: looks like it

@cloakndagger: We need a way to stay in touch

@brains&beauty: I'll be in touch. I know several of you IRL

@truthsleuth: You do?

@workingmom: I'm closing down the chat for today. Check the message boards for more info.

[end transcript]

Chapter 13

"Some of them think the killer is one of them. Most of them are ready to go dark."

Two hours after the abruptly terminated chat between the Deep Freeze Detectives, Sam met with Zielinski, Lopez, Nichols, and Carlisle at the Gramercy Park Precinct, along with an IT specialist and computer forensic analyst named Jessica Holder.

"They're afraid they're being stalked," Sam continued. "I tried to make it sound like nonsense, but what if it's true?"

"Do you think the killer was part of the chat today?" Carlisle asked.

"Hard to say. We were over and out inside fifteen minutes."

"We need a motive," Lopez said. "I mean, beyond Sam's initial assessment. The killer could be a thrill-seeker or power-tripper, sure. But what is it about these people and their true crime hobby that angers our villain? Is he or she tied to one of the cold cases Levy and Wright talk about on the show?"

"Some of the chat members brought that up," Sam said. "The current unsolved case concerns a child named Kyle Jordan. He was abducted from his day school twenty years ago out on Long Island. His body was found three days later in a ditch not far from his house. The perpetrator was never caught. There were charges of sloppy detective work and fingers pointed at everyone from the kindergarten teacher to an out-of-favor uncle. Based on the little I know, no one has come close to naming the killer."

"And the web detectives think they can solve it?" Nichols asked, her skepticism plain. "They may have an inflated sense of their abilities."

"Or the killer does," Sam replied. "Which might make said killer impatient with the process."

"So, the response is to torture and kill the amateurs?" Carlisle asked. "Seems a little extreme. Why not trash them on social media?"

The others responded with uneasy laughter.

"Officer Holder is our tech expert," Zielinski said. "Maybe she came up with some clues to further enlighten us. Officer Holder?"

The willowy young woman pushed her oversized frames up to the bridge of her nose and nodded enthusiastically, which promptly sent the glasses back down her nose.

"Detective Zielinski asked me to print out the real time transcript and make you copies, even though he knows I hate killing trees." She handed out neatly bound packets to each of the team members. "This is a copy of the transcript from today, along with whatever information I could get on the participants. Not much in such a short time. I browbeat Ravi Patel into helping."

"The Deep Freeze sound engineer is also the webmaster?" Carlisle asked.

"Yeah, and that's part of the problem. A good admin will check the logs. An inattentive one might not. It's easy to set up the logging, but not everyone follows through. I'm sure Ravi is terrific at producing the podcast, but the website shows more than a little neglect as far as security is concerned. I'll bet they got an outside consultant to set up the message boards and chat rooms."

"That explains how someone might get the names of the other participants in the chat," Lopez said. "Ravi wouldn't notice a data breach if he wasn't checking."

"We ought to check out the web designers," Zielinski suggested.

"I did that first thing," Holder replied. "The company is totally legit, no obvious issues, plenty of clients. They aren't responsible for maintenance and there's no evidence they've been back inside."

She looked down at her iPad, and the glasses slid farther. "Here's what I have. Six of the people on today's chat made some effort to hide their IP addresses. The most common way to do that is to use a VPN address and the TOR browser. You don't get a hundred percent protection, but it's pretty good for the average civilian. A couple of people logged in from public computers in coffee shops or hotels. Someone named cloakndagger is operating behind a firewall as thick as anything I've ever run into."

"So, of the eleven people on the chat today—" Sam began.

"You mean fifteen."

"I don't understand."

"Eleven people participated," Holder said. "Four more logged on but never commented. The chat software doesn't list the participants. That's an odd glitch, easily fixed," she added.

"The front end is opaque, but the back end is leaky," Zielinski said.

Holder beamed. "Exactly."

"If it's that easy to get the names ..." Nichols began.

"Then Levy and Wright were holding out on us," Carlisle finished.

Holder circulated copies of two more pages. "These are people I've identified already. The list includes Lieutenant Tate, who is @countyhunter and @crimejourno, a.k.a. Tom Levy, who was lurking. Three more who stayed quiet may have been shy, but they were easy to discover. You'll notice almost everyone used a personal email to log on. I don't know what they do for a living yet or how they spend their Sundays, but I can get that."

The next page began with another category labeled as "not yet identified." Holder had listed five screen names: brains&beauty, seenitall, puzzlemaven, cloakndagger, and notmydayjob.

"All of these people commented," Sam noted. "They must be secure about the steps they've taken to hide their identities."

"They haven't met me," Holder said with a straight face.

"Why do I get the feeling the names you've already traced are the least likely to be the killer's?" Carlisle groused.

"We still have plenty of potential suspects to work on," Lopez remarked.

"Unless the killer isn't masquerading as a Deep Freeze Detective," Nichols said.

The others groaned.

"Let's stick to what we have to work with," Zielinski said. "We can begin with the five people who've been less than forthcoming about their identities. They may have something to hide; they may not. I'm concerned that these last two murders are so close together. So is the assistant chief of detectives, by the way. She wants to meet with me tomorrow, along with someone from the mayor's office."

He turned to Holder. "I'd tell you to take all the time you need, Officer Holder, but we have a busy killer and a city on edge."

"What's next?" Sam asked.

"As soon as we have information on the suspects, we'll begin to interview them. Sam, we have a behavioral analyst we use. Maybe you can work with her to come up with a profile on our killer."

"Sure. Whatever you need." She caught a glimpse of Nichols wearing her usual glower.

"The rest of you may or may not be called in this weekend. For sure we'll hit the ground running Monday morning. So, clean up the rest of your caseloads as much as possible."

Chapter 14

Sam took the train back to her aunt's house. She felt discouraged by the turn of events. First, she'd failed to keep herself from becoming too invested in this case. Then she'd drawn undue attention to herself. Finally, her foray onto the chat room had produced very little. Three people had died over a period of ten days, two while she was in town, one while she was supposed to be helping. One of her team members was not happy with her.

Worst of all, she was now relegated to desk work.

The ever-present roar of traffic on the Grand Central Parkway greeted Sam as she exited at Astoria Boulevard. The wind pushed her back a step, as did the pungent mix of spiced food and exhaust fumes that filled her nose. Damp air from low-hanging clouds surrounded her.

City gloom was different than country gloom. She'd lived through plenty of gray days with help from a warm comforter. What she missed was the absolute silence that had been a regular feature of her life since leaving Nashville five years and two jobs ago. Here among throngs of people, it was possible to feel not just solitary but abandoned.

On the other hand, when had she not felt that way? She was in her mid-thirties, and she couldn't find the balance between lonely and alone. She hated the first and required the second.

Her eye, ever trained for an anomaly, went to a figure across the street. Average height, on the slender side, probably male, but the black hoodie made it difficult to tell. A mask and sunglasses worked as a disguise and had the advantage of being ordinary these days.

Whoever it was had ridden the train with her, standing several feet away in the crowded car before exiting at the same stop. Still, she wouldn't have noticed anyone in the crush of commuters except the person carried no visible accessories, no briefcase, pocketbook, backpack, or gym bag. Not even a phone, at least not one that had made an appearance. That was unusual.

Her gut tightened. The instinct, she'd learned, was more than a feeling. Her subconscious was hard at work, synthesizing her experience and her training to help her react appropriately to the situation. In this case, to warn her.

She deliberated whether to walk eight blocks out of the way to lose herself and her tail in Astoria Park. She decided to stick to the streets, crowded despite the inclement weather, with an assortment of people coming to and from work.

For the next half hour, she made her way around Astoria, alternately looking into shop windows and moving with purpose. The figure stayed behind her, adjusting speed, sometimes stopping to browse but always keeping pace.

At one point, Sam went into a bodega and bought a few items. When she emerged, she saw the black hood reflected in the window of the spice shop directly opposite.

As she continued to dodge her pursuer, Sam considered various scenarios. She could turn around and confront him. She had a badge, though her weapon was back at Rosa's. Just as well, considering the number of people out and about. She could call 9-1-1, but by the time help arrived whoever was following her would be long gone. She could try to engineer a reverse tail, become the hunter instead of the hunted. It might unnerve her stalker.

She had no intention of leading him to her aunt's house.

The fading daylight made the person in black difficult to see. Lengthening shadows provided cover. She had to make a move.

She found herself on Broadway and spotted the awning for Pawsitively Purrfect. Open until six, which meant Vincent and Melinda were probably getting ready to close. She ducked into the store. Vincent came over to greet her, broom in hand.

"I need a back way out," Sam said.

Vincent didn't ask questions, just pointed to the supply room. "There's a door to Thirty-Second Avenue and a lot of ways to cut through the neighborhood once you exit," he said.

"Thanks." Sam rested her hand on his arm. "Close early."

He gave her a thumbs up. "Will do. Stay safe."

Sam made a beeline for the supply room. Cinnamon, the matriarch of the feline family, looked up, her gold eyes searching. Sam nodded. Maybe the cat was acting as her spirit animal. She'd take all the help she could get.

She pulled her cap out of her bag, tucked her hair underneath, and hit the street. She cut her way through tightly packed buildings, zigzagging in a northwest direction until she reached her aunt's block. She stood back from the light that came from the lobby of a newly rehabbed apartment building and watched the street for another fifteen minutes before she slunk into Rosa's place.

Her aunt had left the hall light switched on. She'd mentioned dinner with friends, which meant she was out. Sam picked up a flashlight from the side table and headed upstairs to get her weapon. Then she crept through the house, checking in closets and under furniture. Only when she'd closed every curtain and lowered every shade did she turn on more lights.

In the kitchen with her gun and her phone on the table and a glass of Chianti in her hand, Sam reviewed the events of the last hour. She'd been followed. The who didn't matter as much as the why. Maybe the killer was targeting her, but it didn't make sense. Why her and not a regular member of the DFDs? For that matter, why not follow Danny Carlisle or Ron Zielinski or Margarite Lopez? To figure that out, she'd need a motive. The team had yet to come up with a solid theory as to why the killer was after fans of the true crime podcast. Or at least a theory that made logical or intuitive sense to Sam.

What if the mystery figure's appearance was unrelated to this case? What if this afternoon's incident was tied to what happened at her brother's wedding all those years ago? Who knew why Sam was really in New York? Who might have a problem with her efforts to resolve her doubts or answer questions about what happened decades earlier?

She should call Terry, Sam reasoned. He would be calm, reassuring, and supportive. All the things that would be good for her. All the things she needed right now.

Instead, she picked up her phone and called Danny Carlisle.

He pulled up twelve minutes later. Sam heard the meaty growl of a motorcycle from the kitchen. She jumped up and ran to the front window to see Carlisle climb off his bike, stick a NYPD sign on the handlebars, and bound up the stairs with two helmets.

She opened the door and waved him inside. She expected him to be dressed in leather, but he wore the same jeans and blazer combination with the same pin.

"Thanks for coming," she said. "You made great time. I'm sure everyone in the neighborhood heard you arrive. Is that a Harley?"

"I'm close by, I'm not known for subtlety, and yes, it's a 2015 XG750. Are you all right? Should I do a sweep of the house or the block?" He put a hand lightly on her arm, concern in his eyes.

Sam felt her anxiety ebb, replaced by a more powerful current she hoped she could ignore.

"I'm fine, Danny. And you don't need to search the area. I lost my tail back on Thirtieth Avenue. I did check the house and walked the perimeter when I got here."

"If you're sure." He followed her into the kitchen, saw the gun and the glass of wine, still half full. "Where's your aunt?"

"Out to dinner. I just got a text from her. Her party of four turned into a group of twelve. They're having a wonderful time and have made arrangements for escorts home." She shook her head. "I'm not sure what that means, but it's oddly comforting."

"Speaking of dinner, I hope that's not yours." Carlisle pointed to the wine.

"Well, I'd *prefer* something more substantive."

"Good. I know a place."

"Let me change." In response to his skeptical reaction, she added, "I'll dress cycle-appropriate. Help yourself to some wine. Drink fast, though. I'll be done in a flash." She snatched up her gun. "I assume at least one of us is armed?"

He grinned. "You assume correctly."

Sam took the stairs two at a time. She disarmed her weapon and locked it away, threw water on her face, pulled a brush through her hair, and swiped on mascara and lip gloss. Black denim jeans were good for any occasion, she assumed, so she left them on and replaced her blouse with a dark green cashmere turtleneck sweater. At the bottom of the stairs, she grabbed her leather jacket out of the closet.

Carlisle was at the window, wine in hand. He turned around with a wide smile. "When you said you didn't need much time, I didn't realize just how fast ..." He stopped talking.

Sam put a hand to her hair. "What? Do I have tissue paper stuck somewhere?"

Carlisle shook his head as if to break a spell. "You're perfect, Tate. Bring a mask and proof of vaccine. Let's go."

Chapter 15

During the short ride, Sam felt her anxiety drain away. Something about the wind in her face, the smell of his jacket, the sense of adventure, the security presented by his broad back. She didn't want to think too hard about any of it; she just wanted to stay where she was for as long as she could.

Unfortunately, the ten-block ride was over before she knew it. They pulled up to a rustic-looking restaurant with twinkling lights and an awning that advertised artisanal food as well as brick-oven pizza. An animated crowd blocked the entryway and spilled over onto the sidewalk.

"I don't suppose you made reservations on the off chance you'd need to take a distressed colleague to dinner," she said.

"I know the owner," he said. "Come on." He grabbed her hand as if it were the most natural thing in the world. The jolt that ran through her at that simple gesture stopped her from replying or even reacting.

She yanked up her mask and allowed herself to be pulled through the crowd.

"Danny!" The bartender cried out before they reached the entrance. "Get in here. Does Tony know you're coming? Oops, I guess he does."

"*Amico! Come va?"* The booming voice belonged to a broad-chested man with pale eyes and salt and pepper hair who enveloped Carlisle in a bear hug, then stepped back, still holding Carlisle's arm. "Hah," he said. "You're still wearing it."

"Always. Can you squeeze us in, Tony?"

"Of course," the man replied. "For you and your friend." He grinned and squeezed her hand.

"I'm Sam. Your place is lovely, and it smells delicious."

"Wait until you taste the food. And the wine! Come."

He seated them at a small table in the back, complete with a melting candle in the center. The lighting was lower and softer, the location out of the way of the energetic servers and ebullient diners who filled the restaurant.

Sam pulled off her mask. She leaned in and whispered, "We're starring in *The Lady and the Tramp*."

Carlisle chuckled. "Tony's may be long on atmosphere, but the food does not play second fiddle, trust me. We'll do more than spaghetti."

The waiter appeared almost immediately to present a bottle to the table. "Compliments of Chef Tony," he told them. "I'll just uncork it and let it breathe. Oh, and you won't need menus, either."

When he left, Sam allowed her face to register surprise. "Wow. What did you do to deserve a 2010 Brunello from San Filippo Le Lucere?"

"You know your wines?"

"Only the ones I can't afford. I tasted this a decade ago at a fancy dinner. It's only gotten better and more unaffordable with age. Seriously, how do you know Tony?

"I saved his son. He gifted me this pin." He pointed to his lapel. "It's an Italian horn, which is supposed to protect against evil. Tony being Tony, this one is eighteen carat gold. I had to clear it with my superiors, since they disapprove of officers who accept gifts.

Fortunately, they made an exception when Tony showed up to insist."

"Does it work?"

He laughed. "I'm still here."

A few minutes later, the waiter returned with glasses and the uncorked bottle. The heady aroma reached Sam even before she lifted the glass to inhale.

"Cheers," Carlisle said. They toasted and sipped. Sam sighed, transported by the superb wine.

"Thank you for this," she said. "I'm not sure why I got spooked this afternoon. It's not the first time I've been followed."

"Tell me what happened."

She described her encounter with and evasion of the mystery man. A small plate appeared in front of each of them and they paused to enjoy salmon tartare.

"Do you think it had to do with this case?" Carlisle asked. "I don't know why the killer would follow you in particular, but nothing much about this case makes sense." He tapped his forehead. "Unless you have another case that followed you here. Do you?"

He was, Sam admitted, an incredibly handsome man, and his attention was complete and unwavering. She decided food would address the fluttering in her stomach. And more wine. Especially if she was going to respond to his question.

"My family members were the victims of a crime years ago." She spoke as if she were reading from an old file. "They caught the perpetrator. Case closed."

She gulped, fighting against panic. She'd never talked about her past with anyone except her shrink and Terry. And now a good-looking colleague who was nevertheless a stranger.

"But it's not closed for you," Carlisle said, his voice gentle.

She didn't reply.

"Sam." He reached across the table and took her hand. "I won't ask you any questions you don't want to answer. We can change the subject and talk about me. Which, believe it or not, is not my favorite subject, no matter what people tell you."

His remarks had the desired effect. She made a sound between a snort and a giggle, and her mood lightened. She thought about moving her hand. It seemed perfectly content to rest under his larger one. The waiter reappeared to refill their empty glasses and her hand returned to her side of the table.

"More facts," Carlisle continued. "Born forty-one years ago in Riverhead on Long Island. Mom is a retired schoolteacher. Dad owned a bar, which he sold for a tidy sum and a promise that he could get his first drink on the house. Two uncles and an older brother are cops out on the Island. My younger sister lives in the city, is married with two kids, and is a high-powered tech entrepreneur with a patient husband. Carlisle may sound English, but Dad is second-generation Irish, and Mom comes from a large Italian family."

"Sounds like my family!" The words popped out before Sam had a chance to catch them.

A bemused smile crossed his face. "I wouldn't have guessed by your name." He put up a hand. "What else? I graduated from City College, spent a year in Iraq with the National Guard. The less said about that, the better. Then a little time in Europe. I came back, passed through the academy, joined the force, and here I am."

"You didn't get on the bureaucratic fast-track, I gather?"

He laughed. "I've gotten flack about that from nearly everyone about pushing myself up the ladder. Right now, I'm happy where I am. On the other hand, I'm not getting any younger."

Fortified by wine, Sam asked her next question. "Wife? Kids? Significant other?" Her list of questions earned her a guffaw.

"All right, then. Let's get to it. Engaged twice and married once. Both women were terrific, and I didn't deserve either of them. I cheated on my fiancée and stayed true to my wife, but she was never gonna believe me. No kids, although she remarried pretty quickly and has twins." He shrugged. "Now I live in Long Island City in a swanky apartment I snagged under a rent-controlled loophole. Close enough to work. Also close enough to my family that we can get together for special occasions, but not so close that they drop in unannounced."

"Sounds ideal," Sam said. She meant to tease him, but the words came out sounding wistful.

"You'd think so. Anyway," he picked up his wine glass and toasted, "let's hear about you."

"Here are the salads," Sam announced with relief.

Carlisle grinned. "And the waiter, since we've apparently finished the first bottle."

He approved the second offering, a flavorful red from Puglia. While they sampled the arugula with shaved parmesan and limoncello dressing, Sam tried to figure out what she could talk about now that she'd hinted at a family tragedy. Maybe she could pretend it hadn't come up.

She chose to talk about her life post-university. Plenty there to keep him entertained.

"That's a pretty interesting life you've led," Carlisle said when she'd paused. "UCLA to country singer to Army lieutenant. Sounds like my early adulthood. I mean, the trying things out part. Where was romance in all this? You must have some stories to tell."

"Um, not so much. I was engaged, but my fiancé was killed in a car crash right after I entered the academy."

"I'm sorry."

"It was a while ago. After that, I let a long time go by. I thought I had something going with someone else, a colleague. We moved closer to each other, but it was still long-distance. His work and my work and COVID ... I can't tell if it's survived or not."

"Distance is hard on relationships."

"It doesn't help that I'm something of a moving target, both physically and emotionally," she admitted.

He reached for her hand. "Maybe you've been trying to get to something. Or away from something. Memories of your fiancé or Afghanistan, or something to do with what happened to your family."

Sam pulled back. "It's not that easy—"

"Sam, if I overstepped—"

"It's fine. It's just ..." She took a deep breath and let it out. "You might not believe it, but I wasn't always Sam Tate."

"Tell me more. I mean, if you want to."

"Here it is." She gripped her wine glass. "I was born Sophia Russo of Queens, New York. I had a much older brother and, I just discovered, another one who died before I was born. When I was nine, I went to my big brother Stefan's wedding. Actually, I was part of the wedding party as a maiden of honor. Happiest day of my life." She stopped.

"And then?" Carlisle asked in a gentle tone.

"Then a crazy man who'd been stalking the bride, Nicole, showed up with a gun and shot a lot of people before he was stopped. The best man and I were the only survivors in the wedding party. My father died trying to save me. My mother was hit in the head trying to save him. She suffered a traumatic brain injury and has been in a care facility in Delaware for years. She doesn't speak or remember."

Carlisle opened his mouth, but she put up a hand.

"There's more. I went to live in Delaware with my aunt and uncle, left them for college at eighteen, and returned just once a year to see my aunt and visit with my mother. I changed my name. I tried to put it all behind me. Then, several years ago, I started having nightmares about a second gunman at the wedding. I went to see a therapist in Nashville. She was shot to death three months later. My aunt got cancer and I moved east from Tennessee to be near the mother who doesn't know me. Oh, and this gunman I thought I saw at the wedding may still present a danger to me."

Carlisle stared at her. His mouth worked, as if it were trying to form the right words.

"That's a lot for you to handle by yourself, Sam Tate."

"I'm not by myself. I have some support."

"You need an army of supporters," he declared. "What about family?"

"My Aunt Rosa is my father's older sister. I'm learning things from her. No one left on my mother's side, except her cousin Karen. We only met once, at my aunt's funeral. I need to talk with her."

He leaned forward, started to reach for her hand, thought the better of it, and grabbed his wine glass instead. "Is that why you spoke with Andy Mills? Because he was on the force back in ninety-four? Because you need him to help you investigate?"

"It's not a formal investigation. I just want to pick his brain, find out what he remembers, try to see what I remember or what I may have missed."

"You're not an amateur, Sam. But this sounds incredibly dangerous."

Sam twirled her glass. She wanted to answer without appearing defensive. "There's no immediate threat, Danny. Yes, I may or may not be poking around in an old case, but nothing I discover after all this time will have any impact on anyone except me."

And maybe a certain powerful senator, she thought.

"And what if your new stalker is the Dry Ice Killer?" Carlisle asked.

"What happened today felt more performative.," she replied. "For show. To scare me. Maybe you'll all get your own personal stalkers in the next few days."

Carlisle smiled. "True. Or maybe we'll find out he was just trying to get close to the beautiful woman he saw on the N train."

"Says you," Sam replied.

Carlisle clapped his hands. "Now that sounds like a girl from Queens."

The rest of the evening passed quickly, aided by delicious food buttressed by copious amounts of wine. Tony kept dessert light, biscotti and an Amarone for each of them. Sam barely kept from groaning as she sat back.

"I am so uncomfortable and yet so satisfied," she commented.

"Then the evening was a success," Carlisle said as he came around to pull out her chair.

He parked at the end of Rosa's block. "This way, I get to walk the girl home," he said. He held her hand as they strolled down the street, their silence easy. Sam could have been floating for all she knew. For that matter, she could have been sixteen.

At the front step, under the light Rosa had left on, they stood close to each other.

"I'm usually pretty good with my impulse control," Carlisle remarked.

"But?"

"But not tonight."

He put a hand to her cheek and bent his face to hers. His kiss was soft, the urgency underneath unmistakable. Sam leaned into the warmth and stopped thinking.

Ten seconds later, they eased apart.

"Thank you for one of the most unexpected and enjoyable nights I've had in some time," he said. He kissed her again, lightly, and trotted down the stairs. At the bottom, he turned and waved.

What just happened? Sam asked herself. They were colleagues. He might be involved with Margarite Lopez. She hadn't worked out her relationship with Terry. She didn't live here.

He hadn't said anything about a next time. It was just a kiss.

Was it?

She tiptoed into the house and checked her messages. She had two texts. One was from Terry.

She texted back:

Just getting home. Tomorrow?

The second text caught her off guard. Karen Halloran, the Boston cousin to her mother and aunt, was coming to New York Sunday and looking forward to seeing her cousin's daughter.

Will wonders never cease? Sam thought.

She asked for details and offered to meet Karen at the train station. Then she took two Tylenols and went to bed to dream of princes with dark hair, dragons with jewels for eyes, and a castle filled with dry ice.

Chapter 16

Tasha Wright checked her watch. Then she checked her phone against her watch. Twelve minutes late. Not an optimal way to begin a meeting.

For good measure, she glanced at the digital clock on the wall of the studio. Everything matched: 9:12 or 21:12, according to the wall clock. For some reason, Tom preferred military time. Ravi found it amusing; she found it annoying. Tom won out, of course. He always did. When it came to professional opportunities. When it came to ratings or his ability to attract female listeners, which was tied to something called a "likeability" factor, according to their new marketing team. Even his messed up personal life, for which he bore some responsibility, seemed to be straightening out. He'd reconciled with his grown daughter. They were having dinner tonight.

Yes, he'd suffered a horrible misfortune. Losing his young son took a terrible toll on him and on his family. He processed his pain by becoming an activist who pushed for everything from safer school release programs to harsher prison sentences for stalkers. Good for him.

His wife handled her grief differently. She found a therapist, joined something called a sorrow circle, and read every book on losing a child she could get her hands on. She turned inward, he turned outward, their young daughter suffered, and so did their marriage. Textbook example of a grieving family torn apart.

Yet he parlayed that tragedy into a successful career as a victims' advocate, a knowledgeable journalist, a civilian "expert" on the emotional costs of cold cases, a popular guest on the talk-show circuit, not to mention cable and internet shows, and finally, a well-regarded author with a best-selling book and another under contract.

Which left her where, exactly? Cohosting a podcast, although she felt like an add-on or an afterthought compared to her more well-known colleague. Dismissed as a burned-out ex-cop despite a more than decent run. Subjected to both scrutiny and constant challenge by the know-it-all web sleuths, none of whom had ever put their lives in danger.

She'd spent the afternoon in the studio with Tom so they could record a "special edition" podcast assuring their listeners that none of them were in danger (a patent lie) and all of them could help (a gross exaggeration).

Not that she expected they'd lose their fan base (well, except through murder). The notoriety from the show's apparent link to the Dry Ice Killer caused a spike in the number of listeners. Activity on the message boards dropped, although a few hardy souls used it to speculate as to which cold case had the killer riled up. The chat was suspended, but Tasha suspected some of them were talking to each other. All of it was temporary, a blip on the way to more success.

And who knows? Maybe one of those DFDs had a knack for actual detective work or a surefire means of prying the truth out of someone. Maybe whoever was meeting Tasha tonight had something substantial to offer, something that made it worth her while to spend a Saturday night at her workplace instead of with someone funny and charming. Like that lawyer she dated last year or the brooding detective who came by the other day. Even his name sounded like a character on a TV drama. Detective Dan Carlisle.

She knew nothing about him, except that he was easily ten years younger and probably a player, with looks like that. Or a loner married to his work. Or actually married, with a flawless wife and two flawless kids he couldn't wait to get home to. Exactly what the lawyer claimed he wanted when he broke up with her. Well, that and a chance to sleep with a woman who carried a gun.

She was feeling sorry for herself, and that wouldn't do. She needed to figure out who was targeting the most active fans and why.

Many of the Deep Freeze Detectives had taken steps to protect themselves with their safeguarded servers and VPNs. Their efforts were largely futile. She had friends on the force and access to some of the brightest minds and the most advanced technology in the world. She was a retired detective, for God's sake. She'd made it her business to gather at least basic information on all of them from day one. She even discovered the identity of @cloakndagger, although when she got to the end of her search, she chose to leave well enough alone. That was a hornet's nest she didn't need to poke.

Tom didn't realize how much data she'd collected. After the detectives visited and especially after the third death and the media coverage, he suggested she sit down with Ravi and help him work up a list. Yeah, right. Ravi was a competent sound engineer, but what he understood about the inner workings of the internet could fit on the head of a pin. He didn't even set up a web log until she reminded him. He never monitored it. She did, though.

She asked Tom about warning the Deep Freeze Detectives privately. He insisted that suspending the chat was all they needed to do. He didn't want to frighten anyone unnecessarily. They argued about it this afternoon. Again, he won.

Most of the chat members and the people who commented on the message boards were sincere types looking for a way to indulge a fantasy or blow off steam. Their interest made her money and gave her something of a purpose. They didn't deserve to be in harm's way, threatened by some crazy person with an ax to grind. She felt a duty to protect them. It was why she became a cop in the first place. Protect and serve.

Tasha couldn't lie to herself: The idea of becoming involved in an ongoing investigation thrilled her. She felt alive, energized. She wanted to nail the person who committed these gruesome murders. Because he, she, or they might be a fan of her show. Because it was the right thing to do. And because she had been a terrific homicide detective and a better than average cold case detective. Because she could use the validation.

Her tea was cold. She reached into her bag and brought out the silver flask her ex had given her for their third anniversary. She couldn't believe they made it that far; they certainly didn't make it much past that point. She never knew what to make of the gift. Was it meant as a loving gesture or an insult? A nod to the stress of their marriage or a fond farewell? Then again, he might have given her a silver baby rattle, as her clueless parents did even after she told them she was forever barren.

It's all in the past, she reminded herself, pouring rum into her cup. Just like the attack that nearly took her life and her career. Everyone told her how lucky she was: to be alive, to be allowed to transfer to a "safer" squad, to stay on the job. She wasn't lucky; she was smart and hardworking and resilient. Who else would come back from an attack like that and keep working another eight years? Some of the men, but then they'd let their emotional wounds fester and put everyone else in danger.

She took matters into her own hands. She saw a shrink. She went to a vocal coach. She stayed out as long as was required and came back by politely insisting she wanted to work. She proved a boon to the Cold Case Squad.

The podcast began as a way to increase her profile. Now it also earned her an income, what with sponsorships and endorsements. Combine that with her pension, and she had nearly enough to start her own elite private investigation firm. Something that catered to a select clientele. Maybe she'd finish her master's degree and become a visiting professor, teaching the finer points of detective work to eager undergrads. Maybe she'd write her own best seller. She just had to make her damaged voice cooperate a little while longer.

Tom didn't seem to understand how capable she was, but one of the chat room regulars obviously did. Which is why the self-styled web sleuth approached her. Not Tom, not the hunky homicide detective or the sour-looking one, not even Sam Tate, the serial killer-hunting sheriff who was recently outed by the press. Tasha Wright, a twenty-seven-year veteran of the NYPD with the battle scars to prove it, was taking this meeting.

The tipster had claimed to have information on the killer and on that person's interest in the show's fans. Maybe, maybe not. The evening could turn out to be a bust. Tasha didn't think this wanna-be detective was someone inclined to waste anyone's time, but who knew? Nor was she worried. Still, better safe than sorry.

She reached into her purse and patted her Glock. Locked and loaded. She'd keep it tucked away for now. No reason to give her visitor a heart attack.

The buzzer sounded at 9:15. Tasha grinned despite herself. She was ready to go to work.

Chapter 17

Sam spent her Saturday nursing a headache and checking obsessively for a text like some lovestruck teenager until her aunt sent her grocery shopping. A long phone call with Terry made her feel momentarily better, then guilty.

She drank as much water as possible, ran until her lungs burned, and took a hot shower. Late in the day, Carlisle sent a short text:

On the Island with family. Last night was amazing. Can lightning strike twice?

Her mood improved. She was still on a high note when she got to Penn Station's Moynihan Train Hall Sunday morning and spotted her mother's cousin. Karen Halloran carried herself with confidence. Her round face was attractively framed by a honey-streaked bob. She was stylishly dressed in suede boots, black pants, and a long sapphire-blue jacket that picked up the color of her eyes and perfectly matched her mask.

Karen hugged her. "I'm so glad to see you."

"Same here. You look like a million bucks."

"There's certainly more of me to love," Karen replied with a laugh, "which thankfully suits my husband. Besides"—she threw out her arms— "it's New York. Everyone is expected to be gorgeous. Speaking of which …"

"Please don't tell me I look tired."

"I was going to say, lovely. Good thing you stand out in a crowd.

Sam grabbed her cousin's rollaway and pointed to the exit. "I called an Uber, which is a form of blasphemy in the city," she explained, "but at least we won't need to stand in line for a cab." She looked at her phone and matched the information to a black Kia waiting in front of the station.

"The Sherry Netherland, please," Karen announced to the driver. "Fifty-Ninth and Fifth Avenue."

"Rosa invited you to dinner," Sam told her. "I didn't know how you'd feel about that."

"I'm fine with it. I just don't plan to sleep on her couch. Anyway, she contacted me. She doesn't beat around the bush, your aunt. She mentioned that you have questions, and I might have answers. Smart woman." Karen smiled.

The Sherry Netherland, with its ornate lobby and high-end stores and eateries, epitomizes an old-fashioned luxury reminiscent of an earlier time. Sam imagined men in fedoras escorting slinky women with cigarette holders. She certainly felt underdressed in pants and a jacket. In addition, something tugged at her brain, something she couldn't place.

"You were here once with your mother," Karen said. "You might have been six."

"I can't remember, but I'm glad you told me. It feels familiar."

Karen checked in and was escorted with her luggage to an upper floor and a spacious room with a view of Central Park.

"Very nice," Sam said.

"I wanted to treat myself. Do you have time for a cup of coffee before you go back to working the case you're pretending not to work?" She patted Sam's arm. "Don't look so surprised. I keep up."

They headed one block over to Café d'Avignon, located at the site of the former Plaza Hotel, now upscale apartments. For every Sherry Netherland that survived, another half dozen landmarks had fallen victim to the changing economy, changing tastes, or a worldwide plague.

The cousins chatted easily over coffee. Just as Sam started to relax into the conversation, she sensed a change. Karen sat back, looking determined.

"Uh-oh, down to business," Sam remarked.

"Your Aunt Rosa said you wanted to reconnect, learn more about the family. I hope you don't mind my asking, but why now? I may now be your mother's closest living relative, but you and I have spoken just once since your aunt's funeral. What's changed?"

"Karen, I—"

"That sounded like an accusation, Sam, and I didn't mean it like that." Karen shook her head. "You've had a lot to sort out over the years. I'm happy you're at the point where you can come to your Aunt Rosa or to me with your questions."

"You're certainly entitled to question the timing, Karen. A couple of years ago, I started having flashbacks. I thought it was work-related, but what I saw in dreams or in my mind tied in with my spotty memories of the wedding. I started seeing a therapist to help me sort through everything. Then with Gillian's death and my move on top of all that ..."

Karen reached across the table and took Sam's hand. "I guessed you were struggling, dear heart. I just didn't understand how much. I'm so sorry."

"It's okay. I just learned I had another brother."

"That must have been a shock."

"It explains my mother's sadness."

"Not all of it, Sam. Colleen missed her side of the family."

"Then why didn't they visit?" Sam demanded. "Why didn't we see them?"

"That's what I'm here to explain." She cleared her throat. "Let's start with a bit of history. Are you familiar with the Winter Hill Gang?"

"Irish mobsters out of Boston?"

"Sommerville. And they were Irish and Italian, which was unusual. They reached the pinnacle back in the seventies. Seemed to own a piece of everything. They were pretty much finished by the time the new century rolled around."

"Okay." Sam tried to imagine where the story was headed.

"My father, George, your mother's uncle, worked for the Winter Hill gang. He was the money guy, as far as I know. Money laundering, fixing the books, whatever else mob accounts did."

Sam knew her mouth was hanging open. "My God, Karen. Did your mother know?"

"I believe she did, although she never admitted it. I didn't find out until Dad told me after he was released from prison. That side trip was Whitey Bulger's doing, by the way."

"The mobster who secretly worked as an FBI informant."

"That's the one. He ratted out plenty of his subordinates. Then he was killed in jail. Karma."

"Oh, Karen, that must have been so hard for you and your mother."

"I was out of the house by the early seventies and happy to be free of whatever was going on between my parents."

"I'm sure your mother hated being forced—"

"Mother wasn't forced into anything." Karen's tone turned sharp. "She liked the lifestyle that came with mob money. Maybe she could fool herself into thinking the men who gathered in her living room were contractors or investors or people who needed their taxes done instead of thieves and murderers. Maybe she could pretend these thugs could make her safe. No, my mother had other reasons for despising my father."

"I don't understand."

"Dad cheated on Mom with his brother's wife, your grandmother Peg. He never publicly acknowledged the product of that union, a son who was half-brother to me and also to your mom and aunt."

Karen might as well have tossed her into a fast-moving current. She felt caught in the churn, unable to get her bearings or make her brain work.

"Your father ..." Sam stopped.

"Was a pariah in every sense of the word."

Sam gripped the edges of the table for stability. "Why didn't you tell me all this before now?"

"It's not exactly material for a Zoom call, dear, unless we're meeting with someone to discuss a screenplay for Netflix."

Sam began to laugh; she couldn't help it. Karen joined in. Soon they were whooping it up to the consternation of the other customers. They managed to quiet themselves only because the waitress looked as if she would happily throw them out on the street.

Karen gulped to stop a final burst of laughter. "Oh, my, that felt good."

"It does sound like a bad film plot," Sam replied. "But with real-world consequences."

"The consequences had everything to do with who my father worked for, Sam. Adultery is generally a family secret, even when a man is cheating with his brother's wife. Perhaps people suspected when Peg got pregnant, or when she claimed she'd had a stillbirth. She stayed with your grandfather and my mother stayed with George. I doubt your father's side of the family had any idea. But the mob connection, well, that rubbed your father the wrong way."

"Aunt Rosa says my dad was under near constant pressure to deal with gangsters," Sam said. "He barely kept the Russo clan out of the action. When my cousin Johnny got hooked by connected loan sharks, Dad and Rosa paid off the debts. Then my uncle Jimmy beat Johnny within an inch of his life."

Karen sighed. "Your father was a proud man."

"So, you found out after George left prison ..."

"2005 or thereabouts"

"And you told Gillian. She could have told me. I was old enough to know the truth." Sam squeezed her eyes against the hot tears that formed. She sounded petulant. She didn't care; she felt cross and worse, shut out.

"You were also old enough to run away from it, Sam," Karen said gently.

Sam dropped her eyes to her lap. "I did a lot of that." She swallowed. "Whatever happened to the illegitimate child?" she asked.

Karen's lips were set in a grim line. "This is where it gets murky. My foolish father, instead of letting Peg contact an adoption agency, told someone in his other family and they arranged a trade."

"A what?" Sam realized she'd raised her voice. "Explain, please," she said more quietly.

"The baby was given to a couple in Providence, Rhode Island, with close ties to the Patriarca family. They were and still are a formidable East Coast mob family with far more power than the Winter Hill Gang ever had. Some agreement was arranged, the terms of which I can't guess. My father claims the family that took in the infant were solid, respectable types who simply wanted a child in their lives."

"A child who would grow up to join the family business."

"I have no idea. Never met him, never went looking for him after George let me know the kid might have support from some bad people. I don't know what he looked like or what they called him. My dad and Peg referred to him as Baby Quinn. Sam, what is it? Drink some water. You look light-headed."

Sam finished her water while Karen waved over the waitress to request more.

"A man who called himself Quinn was spotted in the old neighborhood before the wedding, Karen. My FBI partner located an eyewitness who remembers seeing the same man at the wedding, wearing a brown suit and holding a gun. Same thing I recalled."

"On your block?" Karen exclaimed. "Then at the wedding? Why?"

"I can't say for certain," Sam admitted. "Look." She pulled out an image of Sean Parker she'd printed from his website and handed it across the table.

"Who is this?" Karen asked.

"Sean Parker, our new senator from Maryland. He originally hails from Queens, New York. At least according to his official bio. Does he look familiar?"

The older woman stared at the picture, then looked up. "He has your eyes. Or you have his. That is unusual. It doesn't mean he's my half-brother or your uncle."

"I think he might be."

Karen pressed her fingers into her forehead. After a half a minute, she dropped her hands.

"If I'm following, you believe my father's illegitimate child, raised in Providence, Rhode Island, as Sean Parker by people with ties to an East Coast mob, was seen in the neighborhood where his half-sister lived. This same man appeared at her son's wedding with a gun. Are you suggesting the shooting was a hit job? Or that Quinn was there to kill your family?"

"Again, I don't know. Maybe crazy Arthur Randolph was a diversion or a lucky break or ..." Sam stuttered, searching for a way to transfer the unshakable beliefs to her cousin.

Karen pointed at the picture lying faceup on the table. "This man could be Quinn, Sam. He could be your uncle. The resemblance is uncanny. He may even have been in your neighborhood or at the wedding. Maybe he was carrying a gun. But now, more than twenty-five years later, this man has been elected to the US Senate. So, tell me: What do you want or expect?"

"I want to find out if he was at the wedding. I want answers about what he did or what he saw and whether he is still involved in my life now and why? Because someone is, Karen. Someone tied to those events. Of that I am convinced. Someone who opened the sealed records of my testimony as a child."

"What could Parker possibly hope to gain? What is his endgame?"

"I don't know, Karen," Sam said. "But I suspect I might be part of it."

Chapter 18

Karen saw herself off Monday morning, which gave Sam time to get in a run and a yoga routine. She'd been asked to meet at Zielinski's precinct, though she wasn't sure why. Did Carlisle report her stalking before she had a chance? Was there another victim she didn't know about? A breakthrough? Was she even working the case, other than to sit in on chats and report back?

Terry texted, no doubt a response to the long email she'd sent last night concerning the revelations her cousin brought with her from Boston. She punched in his number.

"How did you sleep?" he asked.

"The usual," she replied. "As I recall, my newly acquired dead brother did battle with my newly acquired living half-uncle while my mother and I watched."

"Sounds like quite the bonding experience."

"You know, my memories of my mother are mixed, Terry. She was always kind, always gentle. She could be fun, too. She'd sing and recite little poems. She read to me. I remember hearing her laugh. But she also carried a great sadness with her. Now I understand."

"It's a hard burden to bear."

"God, my childhood sounds like a soap opera, what with gangsters, ghosts, and enough family secrets to fill a vault." Sam finished her coffee and went to get more.

"Doesn't sound like your dad's side of the family was part of all that."

"I don't think my mother was either, at least not the criminal part." Sam chewed her lip. "My dad kept her away from her family for the most part. I hope he didn't blame her for one or two rogue relatives. Or that she resented him for taking such a hard line."

"Maybe that's something you can discuss with Rosa."

"Maybe. After I make sure she's not the Dry Ice Killer's next target."

"I can't tell if you're joking or not."

Sam sighed. "I'm joking. Sort of."

"I don't need to tell you to take care, do I?"

"I will, Terry. I absolutely promise."

"Okay. I gotta run." He went quiet a couple of seconds. "Sam, call anytime. About anything."

"I will."

Another small silence. Then: "I love you."

She waited too long. "I—" she began, but he'd already hung up.

At least the commute was relatively smooth, putting Sam inside the 13th Precinct building at 8:30 a.m. Zielinski greeted her as she exited the elevator. He pointed to the conference room, where she saw bagels, cream cheese, butter, and a hot pot she figured was coffee.

"What's all this?" she asked, dropping her nylon shoulder bag onto the nearest chair.

"We feed our own," he said. "Which means you, temporarily. You're officially a consultant to the NYPD, retroactive to last Tuesday. The offer even includes a nice little stipend. The agreement goes week to week. Everyone understands you have a job as a senior officer with another police force in another state." He held out a two-page document, his grin uneasy.

Sam didn't take it. Something about his discomfort made her hesitate. She folded her arms across her chest.

"Thanks for going to bat for me, Ron," she said. "I appreciate it. But last week, I was a distraction. Now I'm not?"

"Maybe someone upstairs got smart."

"What does that mean? Who is the someone? Because if they're looking for a symbol or a scapegoat, I'm not interested in either role."

"It's not like that," Zielinski protested. "The brass got caught out last week. Then cooler heads prevailed."

"Along with an influential someone."

"So what? It's a good idea as far as I'm concerned." He reached out again; this time, she accepted the papers and scanned them.

"This says I'll be a special consultant to the task force investigating homicides by the so-called Dry Ice Killer, working under the supervision of the assistant chief of detectives."

"That's just a formality. You, me, and Carlisle are still the primary investigators. Lopez and Nichols will provide support as needed and if they're not pulled away. We'll be adding other investigators from other bureaus, also as needed, and a couple of tech and forensic specialists."

"Lopez and Nichols aren't going to like this."

"They'll understand it's just bureaucracy. Won't even go into effect until next week. Maybe we'll catch the bad guy by then."

Sam couldn't pinpoint her hesitation. She enjoyed working this case. It was only for another week or so. She'd get paid.

She held the papers to her chest. "I'm sure it's fine. I just want to take a minute to read this more carefully."

"Go ahead. I think you'll find it's straightforward. I want to get everything on the table at the meeting."

Sam read the document twice more. "Okay," she told Ron as she scribbled her signature. "This will work."

"Work for what?" Carlisle asked, sauntering into the room. "Come on, now. It isn't nice to keep secrets."

He made a beeline for the food, favoring Sam with a smile. She felt her stomach flutter. She covered it with a giggle, as if he'd shared a terrifically funny joke with her.

Lopez entered next, dressed in all black. Nichols followed, again in a suit, a subtle herringbone that still managed to look like a uniform.

"Assuming you can eat and meet at the same time," Zielinski said, "let's get started. First, I want to see what Officer Holder has for us. Welcome."

Holder brought a welcome energy into the room. She wore her hair down, which emphasized her relative youth. The large eyeglass frames, which she obviously hadn't tightened since the last meeting, still threatened to slip off.

"Hi, everyone. I did more digging over the weekend. First, I expanded the list of Deep Freeze Detectives to include everyone who was on the last three chats. That added another eight names, including our three victims. I think we can safely say these are the active members. Based on the content, these chats seem more social than work focused. Then again, it's a hobby, not a job. There are a few impatient types that keep trying to hold the group to the topic at hand, meaning discussion about the Kyle Jordan case. Even so, the group has come up with little of substance."

"Unsurprising," Sam said. "I didn't see much on the message boards beyond wild speculation."

Holder nodded. "At least now we have the names behind the email addresses for nearly everyone, along with physical locations, occupations and such."

"Nearly everybody?" Carlisle asked.

"I ran into a wall with those five I mentioned on Friday. Or, in the case of cloakndagger, into a tank. I received a 'cease and desist' warning from the office of Director of National Intelligence."

"You spooked a spook," Carlisle cracked to uneasy laughter around the table.

"Let's leave that name aside for now," Zielinski suggested. "What about the others?"

"The trails to the other four—puzzlemaven, seenitall, notmydayjob and brains&beauty—all end at the digital equivalent of a postal box. The three big digital post offices are actually managed by one company. We'd need warrants to go further, although ..." she looked at Zielinski before continuing. "I know someone who works there who owes me a favor. Maybe I can get in the back door the old-fashioned way."

She caught Zielinski's frown. "Not by hacking, sir, by asking."

"Do that, then," Zielinski asked. "As far as the rest of the research, will you want help?"

"Could make things go faster," Holder admitted.

Sam raised her hand. "Count me in."

"Me, too," Lopez added.

"If needed," Carlisle volunteered.

Nichols took her time. "However it works out," she finally added.

"We'll get right back to you, Jessica," Zielinski said, which was her signal to leave.

"We ought to be looking to see if any of our chat room members have a tie to the judicial system," Lopez suggested.

You mean as cops, criminals, judges, lawyers, that kind of thing?" Carlisle asked.

"More like regular citizens who were victims and went to the system for help."

"Where are you going with this, Margarite?" Zielinski asked.

"The easiest thing to imagine is that our person is also Kyle Jordan's killer. It could also be someone who hates what's happened with the case."

Carlisle barked a laugh. "You can add a couple of cops to the suspect pool. Not all of us think inexperienced amateurs should be working even cold cases."

"Then why would a killer target them, when the pros can't even catch him or her?"

"Good point, Margarite," Zielinski said.

"Which brings me to a larger point," Lopez went on. "The Kyle Jordan case got a lot of attention from law enforcement, from private groups, from the media and the true crime hobbyists."

"True," Carlisle said. "Cute kid, suburban kid, white kid, wealthy, influential parents. A made-for-media story."

"Right. Kids disappear or die all the time. Their cases don't capture the public's imagination like this one did. Justice isn't always served. If you were one of those parents, how would you feel?"

"You think the killer could be a parent?" Carlisle asked.

"Or a friend or relative of a victim who fell through the cracks."

"Why not start by punishing the podcast hosts and creators?" Sam asked. "They're the ones who seem to be profiting from their choices as to which cases get aired."

"Maybe he's working his way up," Carlisle said.

Nichols looked up from her notebook. "Wasn't Tom Levy's kid snatched off the street right around 9/11?" she asked. "Maybe he believed the slow response harmed the chances of finding his son or his killer. Last month was the twentieth anniversary of the attacks and his son's disappearance. Maybe he was triggered. It's possible he's not a victim in this instance but a perpetrator."

"I don't buy it," Carlisle countered. "No one would fault any responders during a crisis, least of all a crime reporter."

"Don't forget, he also got a lot of attention for his son's case," Lopez added. "He's not the one with a beef."

"Okay," Nichols said. She bit her lip, dropped her eyes to her notepad, and white-knuckled her pen. No one noticed except Sam.

"I like your angle, Margarite," Zielinski was saying. "Our killer could be someone close to a victim whose case has gone cold."

"We have to consider that our killer has help," Sam added.

"What kind of help?" Nichols asked.

"Maybe they're not pushing dry ice down anyone's throat. Maybe they're buying it. Or procuring other supplies, or helping the killer choose the victims or even finding other ways to cover for the killer. Misdirects, red herrings."

"So maybe the helpful associate is on the chat," Carlisle mused.

"Worth pursuing," Zielinski said. "Margarite, do you mind working with Jessica this morning to vet the names? It'll speed up the information collecting so we can get on with speaking to everyone."

"You got it."

"I'll join you," Sam volunteered. She and Lopez fist bumped.

"I'll take a run at our friendly podcasters this time around, just to make sure they're not holding out. Danny, since you've already met them, why don't you join me?"

"Sure."

"I can join you." Nichols stood.

"Detective, do you mind working with Tate and Lopez on the identification? That's the critical part of the work this morning."

"Right," Nichols replied.

Sam thought of a pot simmering over a low flame.

Zielinski made a show of clearing his throat. "Ah, there's another matter we need to discuss. It concerns recommendations from the assistant chief's office as to how she wants us to proceed with the investigation." He repeated what he'd told Sam, then asked for questions. There were none.

"So, everybody is clear?" Zielinski asked.

"Sure," Carlisle said. "We do what we do. Sam gets a stipend. The higher ups decide if they like how we're doing. After which we keep doing our thing or not.

Meanwhile, Sam goes or maybe she stays, and Lopez and Nichols work on something with less oversight."

"Danny ..."

"It is what it is, Ron."

"Looks like you're with us, Chloe," Lopez said. "I'll see if I can hold on to this room for another couple hours and bring Holder back in." She walked out without so much as a glance at the two men.

Carlisle's telephone pantomime—*call me or I'll call you?*—temporarily lifted Sam's spirits, until she glanced at Nichols. The young woman was glaring at her with such venom that Sam stood up and walked out of the room.

It was only nine thirty in the morning and already it felt like a very long day.

Chapter 19

Lopez met Sam outside the conference room. "I noticed you throwing me sympathy looks while Zielinski was telling us the big news," she said. "Sam, this sort of shit happens all the time. I can't speak for Nichols, but I'm fine with letting everyone try to stop an attention-seeking serial killer while I work on the regular old homicides."

"Oh, I can speak for Nichols. She hates me."

Lopez chuckled. "The girl has issues, that's for sure."

"What kind of issues?" Sam asked.

Lopez waved her hands. "Let's not even go there. I'd much rather get the inside scoop on how you went from PR pariah to flavor of the week."

"Ron led me to believe someone intervened on my behalf."

"Oh-ho, help from above. Any idea who?"

Sam thought she might, but the notion was so disturbing she kept bouncing away from it. "I'm not sure," she said instead.

"Well, someone is high enough up there to flip the story from scandal to brilliant tactical move. That's a good thing." She laughed lightly, then switched to a stage whisper. "Ever wonder who outed you to the media in the first place?"

Sam glanced into the now-empty conference room. "I have my suspicions."

Lopez followed her gaze. "Doesn't matter now." She brightened. "On an unrelated topic, what's with you and the other more charming Queens detective? And don't say 'nothing' or ask what I mean. I got eyes, *chica*."

Sam's face flooded with color. "Margarite, it isn't ... I mean, I don't know what it is or if it's anything. Probably just some silly flirtation. I'm not here long. And I would never get between anything that might be going on between you and Danny—"

Lopez roared with laughter.

"Sam, Sam," she said, wiping her eyes. "I'm gay. Not part-time, sort of, sometimes, recently, or if it suits me. Sappho from the get-go. Fully committed to the identity and, if you must know, one special person."

Sam fumbled for the right words. "Of course. I mean, sure. You don't need to—"

Lopez was grinning. "Hey, you're not the first person who's picked up on the love/hate connection between Danny and me. We have a long and sometimes difficult relationship. Partly because he occasionally conforms to every male stereotype ever, partly because I can be an asshole. Mostly because we love each other. Brother and sister, good friends, call it what you will. But it's not about sex or romance or attraction."

She grew serious. "I will say this. I've seen more than one colleague throw herself onto the rocks for him. Don't get me wrong: He's a good guy, and a loyal friend. But he doesn't know what he wants in the heart department. That can create hard feelings and I don't want to see that happen here. You seem to have your head solidly attached to your shoulders. Please tell me I'm not wrong."

Sam wrapped her arms around herself, a defensive posture she immediately recognized for what it was. She dropped them to her sides. "He's overflowing with charm," she admitted. "He deploys it so effortlessly he may not even be aware of how potent it is. Which only adds to his charm."

"And he's hot," Lopez added.

Sam snorted. "He really is," she agreed. "I guess, between COVID-related isolation and my many unresolved issues, I've become a little conflicted about what I want. Which, if I had a head on my shoulders, would be the one guy who's been willing and able to take on all of my baggage and still find a way to ... to ..."

"To love you." Lopez gave her an appraising stare. "You're talking about the FBI guy, aren't you? The one who helped you back in Tennessee. Ron mentioned him one time. Not sure how much he knew, except he seems to be an even better detective than I give him credit for being."

She looked at Sam, her caramel eyes warm. "Maybe I'm not the best relationship expert. Scratch that; I'm definitely not. But I know about need and desire and what feels good in the moment versus what's good in the long haul. Lust is like a drug. Love is like a hot meal. Both of them make you feel good, but only one of them is good for you."

She clapped Sam on the shoulder. "End of lecture. How about we go poke our noses into someone else's business for a while?"

"I've divided the names among the four of us," Holder told the group. "Your job is to find out more about the names on your list: what they do for work, what you can learn about their personal lives, where they live, where they hang out in real life and especially on social media. Use Facebook, Instagram, Twitter, TikTok, YouTube, any of the conspiracy sites, if need be. History is important. I can help with records searches."

"What is countyhunter's backstory?" Sam asked. "I assume you created one."

"That was the fun part," Holder replied. "Your everyday name is Becky Rainey. You work as an assistant in the Nassau County Clerk's Office. You have a moderately active Facebook account, a rarely used Instagram account, and a composite image that fits your Boomer persona."

"Ouch." Sam laughed. "I sound harmless enough. Let's see who else we have."

The diversity represented by the chat group surprised Sam. She'd read that true crime appealed to a broad spectrum of people; she just hadn't realized how broad.

They'd already determined cloakndagger worked for a national intelligence agency. Sam wasn't sure that disqualified the person from consideration as a serial killer. Perhaps someone within the NYPD was working back channels for more information. She could put in a call to Terry, see if he had contacts he could tap.

The rest of the list proved to be easy to work. They stuck mainly to public records, from online white pages to social media accounts. Some of the names led to predictable results. Teacherpreacher was a high school teacher and part-time church deacon. Wknddad was a divorced father of two with a sales job that kept him on the road most of the time.

"That might explain the divorce," Lopez observed.

"Some of these screen names are probably a little on the nose," Lopez said. "Anyone want to bet semperfi is a retired or active Marine?"

"Guess what deepdiver does for a living?" Nichols asked.

"Someone who works underground," Sam suggested. "A miner. A subway operator. A spelunker. Definitely someone with a fondness for profanity and smart-ass comments."

"Good guesses except you're still giving him too much credit for finesse," Nichols replied. "Our guy is literally a scuba-diving instructor out on Montauk named Jeff Radner."

"You got any pictures we can ogle?" Sam asked, prompting giggles.

"You can always check out his Instagram profile," Lopez said. "Hey, I've got the bio for renaissancewoman. She's a twentysomething named Ellen Keeley, who self-describes as a writer/performer/poet/philosopher/yoga instructor/painter/trapeze artist. Her list of jobs is almost as long: property manager, office assistant, sales associate, telephone marketer, and kindergarten teaching assistant."

"Following the dream," Sam said.

"Yeah, but which one?" Holder asked.

They were occasionally stumped. Truthsleuth turned

out to be a physicist and justicewarrior was neither a soldier nor a cop soldier but a court stenographer and mother of five named Esther Torres. Strongcoffee and dedicateddetective were a cab driver and a retired nonprofit executive, respectively.

"Workingmom, Regina Young, has a school-aged son," Nichols interjected. "She lives in the Bronx and works as a dental technician."

"Interesting skill set," Holder noted.

"I'd flag her," Nichols said.

"I'm not seeing anyone with a police record," Lopez observed. "Or any victims of assault. You?"

"Not so far," Holder replied.

"Check the surname Young," Nichols insisted. "I have a feeling."

Holder's fingers moved over the keys. "Damn," she said "The name Cecily Young popped up. Also known as CeCe. Snatched in the Bronx about twelve years ago. She was sixteen. Someone saw her get pushed into a black van. No plates. Never seen again. Wait, I have a picture." She brought up the image of a slender girl with large liquid brown eyes and high cheekbones.

"She's a stunner," Sam said. "Sex trafficking?"

"Or payback if she or her boyfriend ran with the wrong people," Nichols replied. "Does Regina Young have a sister or a daughter?"

"Two brothers and one sister, all alive, only the son," Holder said, squinting at the screen. "Young is her maiden name. Maybe she had a teenaged cousin?

"Did the case receive a lot of attention?" Lopez asked. "Doesn't look like it," Holder replied. "A couple of days in the news, some sort of anniversary event that stopped after a couple of years."

"There you go. Revenge on the dilettante detectives." Nichols sounded triumphant.

"Anything is possible," Sam said.

"And here we are," Holder announced. "A text from my friend that leads to a secure email that requires a password and then leads to another encrypted message. All very hush-hush, but that's why users pay the big bucks."

Sam watched as the technical analyst typed so quickly it was impossible to make out the individual keystrokes. "I imagine these digital services are expensive," she noted.

"Hiding in plain sight always comes with a price," Holder said. Another minute or so passed.

"Got it. Names and addresses for our holdouts." She rubbed the back of her neck and leaned in. "First, we have puzzlemaven, who lives in New Jersey. Married with kids, all of them apparently alive and well. Weird name, though. Branch Loane, with an e."

"Let me guess," Lopez offered. "He's a bank manager."

"Says here he's an author."

"Yes, he is," Sam clapped her hands with delight. "That name is an anagram. Look carefully."

Holder got it first. "Whoa. The mystery writer? I've read some of his stuff."

"Okay, I'll play." Lopez stared at the name. "Hot damn, I see it now." She high fived Sam and Holder. "This guy is famous. What's he doing in a chat room for fake detectives?"

"Looking for source material," Sam replied. "Some of his characters are amateur detectives.

"Can we assume our well-known author is not the Dry Ice Killer?" Holder asked.

"Let's not assume anything," Nichols said. "We should add him to the suspect list."

"Or we could wait for his next book," Lopez said, which earned her a round of guffaws.

"Next, we have seenitall, one Alex Kostakis. He's thirty-six, never married, lives with his invalid mother Helena. That can't be a good sign."

"Let's not think in stereotypes," Nichols warned. "He's not necessarily a closet psychopath living in his mom's basement. He might be saving up for a house or temporarily strapped for cash. This is an expensive city."

Lopez looked over Holder's shoulder and whistled. "He's in an awfully nice basement. This address is in Forest Hills Park."

"Does he have a legitimate job?" Sam asked.

Holder nodded. "He's been gainfully employed as a physician assistant in Mount Sinai's cardiac units for eleven years. I think the hospital PAs make good money, so he's not hurting."

"Maybe he's helping out his sick mother," Lopez said. "Guy could be a saint."

"We can follow up with him," Sam said. "Who's left?"

"Notmydayjob, a.k.a. Kevin Turner, actually has a pretty impressive day job. He's handling program and product development for a private tech company in Maryland with serious government contracts."

Nichols, who had been quietly sipping her coffee, perked up. "Program and product development?" she queried. "That's a broad category. Anything more specific?"

"Nope. He could be developing anything from self-operating electric tanks to 3D rockets to AI soldiers. Maybe it's related to security."

"He could certainly manage to identify a handful of people on a chat room," Lopez said. "Not that it makes him a killer."

"No connection to any crime that I can see," Holder remarked. "He may work from home. Or his parents' home. They live in a pretty upscale part of the city."

"Now that sounds like a suspect," Nichols said. "We should add him to our list."

"How about brains&beauty?" Sam asked.

"Right, I was just getting to that one," Holder said. "Here we go. Teresa Albon. Listed as an entrepreneur, whatever that means." She rolled her eyes. "Last known address was San Francisco; last listed job was in the tech sector. I'm missing a lot of information, like a birthdate or birthplace. Or an image. I'll dig a little more."

Lopez stood and stretched. "We've got several people of interest, including Tom Levy and maybe even the government spy," she said. "Not bad for a morning's work. We should hunt them down before ..."

"Before another body drops?" Holder chirped.

"I was going to say, before the hunting party disbands."

Sam looked up from her phone. "I might have one appointment already," she said. "Brains&beauty wants to meet with countyhunter."

"When?" Nichols demanded.

"Not sure. Time and place to be determined."

"How'd this Teresa person figure out who you were?" Holder asked.

"How did she get your number?" Lopez wanted to know.

Sam looked down at the cryptic text, then back at her colleagues. "How did I go from hunter to prey?"

No one had an answer.

Chapter 20

Sam declined Lopez's invitation to lunch. She wanted to get back to her aunt's and take some time before her coffee 'date' with Andy Mills.

She didn't mention that she also had an evening meeting scheduled with brains&beauty, a.k.a. Teresa Albon, at a storage facility back in Industry City.

Sam couldn't know if the meeting was a trap, a prank, or a previously traumatized woman being cautious. Lopez, if she were told, would insist on going. Worse, she'd be duty bound to report to Zielinski, who would then tell the Queens detectives. Sam would be forced to show up accompanied by a small entourage of armed officers. Not the best way to approach a potential source.

Her aunt was delighted to see her. They chatted briefly over homemade risotto before Rosa left for her doctor's appointment. Sam offered to drive her, but the older woman scoffed at the idea.

"We've both got very busy days, dear heart. We'll connect tonight."

Mills called Sam soon after. "Here's an idea," he said. "Why don't we meet at Antun's? I can pick you up if you don't have a vehicle."

"How did you figure it out?"

"It's not rocket science, Lieutenant Tate. You were in the news just last week, right after I met you. So, not an NYPD detective. And to be honest, one case in Queens Village dominated the others back when I was at the 105. Right around the time I made detective. A mass shooting at Antun's during a wedding. Fourteen dead or injured. Just two survivors in the wedding party, one a young girl who gave testimony and then left New York with relatives. The girl grew into a woman, maybe one who decided to change her name and then become a law officer."

Sam didn't reply.

"I don't know the last time you were back in New York," Mills continued. "I'm gonna guess you've never been back to Antun's. Why you need to revisit this tragedy now I can't imagine. You can tell me or not. I want to help you, though. I'll see what I can pull together and what I can remember. We can meet at the venue or, if you prefer, we can stick with our original plan to meet at the coffee shop close to the precinct. Your call."

"Let's meet at the site," she said before she could change her mind. "I'll drive. Half an hour."

"I'll let them know we're coming by."

Sam pulled her Hyundai out of the lot a few blocks from her aunt's house and plugged in the address. The ride, mostly along Grand Central Parkway, took her through the center of the borough to the section known as Queens Village.

She pulled into the wedding venue's parking lot at 2:45, unsure what she would remember after all this time. The white clapboard building looked smaller than she expected, the inside less grand. Still, it retained its rococo charm, at least as far as the main lobby was concerned. White wainscotting separated the warm peach wallpaper from the periwinkle fleur-de-lis carpeting anchored by a calligraphy-style A. Fresh flowers adorned the space; a massive crystal chandelier hung overhead.

Andy Mills stood at the bottom of the steps that led to the exterior patios. He held a bulky folder in one hand. Next to him a thirtysomething woman with an anxious air tugged at her brunette hair. "Looks like we're headed out back," he said. "Sam, meet Gina Falasco, assistant manager. She'll be our chaperone. Ms. Falasco, this is Sam Tate."

Sam noticed he didn't use her title, probably so Falasco wouldn't be overwhelmed by a police presence.

"I just want to make sure we can address all your concerns," the woman said. She twisted the ring on her finger and forced a smile.

Mills gave a reassuring smile. "Not to worry, Ms. Falasco. This visit doesn't reflect on Antun's in the slightest. Think of it as a, ah, memory prompt."

"I was afraid it had to do with some sort of crime."

Sam and Mills exchanged glances. "I'm trying to remember a face from a long time ago, Ms. Falasco," she said. "From when I was a child. Detective Sergeant Mills is taking me to a few old places to see if something comes back to me."

"Oh, that makes sense," Falasco said, clearly relieved. "If you'll follow me, then. I wasn't sure which of our outdoor areas you wanted to see. Detective Sergeant Mills mentioned the larger one, Montauk Gardens. It's set up for our last outdoor wedding of the season next weekend."

Sam followed her outside, prepared for a jolt. She'd steeled herself to visualize bodies on the makeshift dais at the front of the pathway or hear gunfire and terrified screams.

At first, nothing. She stood at the back of a slatted wood path between rows of white folding chairs that led to the covered section in front of a fieldstone wall. The gardens were dormant, the surrounding walls not as high as she remembered. The neighboring red brick building with the water tower was clearly visible, as were a mishmash of overhead wires. The neighborhood seemed to be forcing its way into the scene.

But what bothered her now must have been all but invisible to the nine-year-old girl in a pink dress made just for her, wearing her grandmother's necklace and almost-grown-up shoes, a girl who'd been honored with the designation "maiden of honor" at her brother's wedding.

The memories began to assert themselves: the guests in their dress-up clothes, the flowers, the large wedding party on the custom platform up front Nicole had specially ordered, two sets of parents in the front row, everyone beaming except for the wild-eyed man in the blue suit near the front and the man with the sunglasses wearing brown and watching from the last row ...

She swayed just as Mills caught her elbow. "You okay, Sam?" he asked, keeping his voice low. "You need some water or something?" Gina Falasco hovered over his shoulder.

"I'm fine," Sam answered. "But I would love a glass of water, Ms. Falasco, if you don't mind."

The woman scurried away. As soon as she'd passed through the doors, Sam turned to Mills.

"Let's see what you have."

He considered her for a second, then opened the folder. "The critical items here are the reports and the diagram. There are some black and white photos, but we don't have to—"

"I want to see it all, Andy."

"Okay, but I gotta ask. Assuming you'd have access through your law enforcement connections to everything I brought in this folder, why haven't you already looked at all this? And why do you need me?"

"I never looked because I hadn't put everything together. I wasn't even allowing myself to think about that day until a couple of years ago. As to the second, you were there."

Mills looked uncomfortable. "Only in a response role," he said. "And it was a long time ago. If you want imperfect recollections, you can ask the wedding guests. Friends of your brother, friends of the family. Relatives."

"I can't ask any of them. They're either very old or ... I don't even know who's still alive." She gulped hard. "I want a cop's-eye view, Andy. An objective breakdown of the crime scene."

Mills considered her statement. "I'll do my best," he said. "Let's start with the report and the diagram. And maybe you'll tell me what you're really after."

They spent twenty minutes walking the small space. Gina Falasco appeared with the water and left again. Sam sat in the back row, where she'd seen the man in the brown suit.

"Were any casings found back here?

"Nope," Mills reported.

Sam was momentarily disoriented. Then she realized that a professional killer could get off a shot and pocket a casing, especially during an assault.

"Why?" Mills demanded. "You think there was a second shooter?"

"There was a second man with a gun," Sam replied. "At least, we located a second eyewitness who confirms seeing a man in the back with a weapon. What neither of us can recall is if he used it."

She moved to the outside chair of the second row on the right, where Arthur Randolph once stood and screamed about love as he tried to destroy as many people as possible.

"How many shell casings were recovered up here?" she asked.

Mills consulted the report. "It says here forty-five."

"Which means he got off forty-five shots and two magazine changes in, what, a minute?"

"That sounds about average for an inexperienced gunman who may have practiced some beforehand. Also, if you're talking effective shooting, two-thirds of his shots went wild, which is also within the realm of possibility."

Sam mimed raising and siting a gun. "Were most of his shots directed at the wedding party on the platform?"

Mills nodded. "It appears that way. He was aiming for the bride and her 'happy friends,' according to his statement. Forensics pulled several bullets out of the pillars. One of them ricocheted off the stone wall and hit a groomsman in the back, killing him instantly." He looked pained. "One witness recalled that Randolph eventually swung the gun around. We know several of the guests on the ground were also injured or killed."

An image of her mother appeared to Sam. She pushed it away. "How was he brought down?"

"A couple of guys rushed him while he was reloading. Twice. The first time, one of them fell, and that allowed Randolph to get off a second round."

"Right." Sam had one more place to stand and she dreaded moving into position. She walked to the front between the two white pillars and looked out.

"And this is where I was found," she stated. "Lying under my father's body."

"Um, no." Mills flipped through the notes. "Police were there within five minutes. No cell phones back then, but someone inside Antun's got through via the land line pretty quickly, all things considered. It was chaos, as you can imagine. The chairs toward the front were all knocked over. Police found you sitting in the back with a couple of older women. Family or friends, maybe. You were in shock."

"I was sitting in the back?" Sam asked. "Can I take a look?"

The notes were handwritten. Clearly no one had gotten around to entering everything into a computer. At least the paper was encased in a plastic sleeve. She scanned the names the interviewing officer had jotted down. No Rosa.

"I'm not sure who these people are. Family or friends on my side or maybe Nicole's." She looked up. "Where did they find my father's body?"

"Where you're standing," Mills said. "Shot in the back. Which means he probably came from up the steps to the dais."

"That makes sense. He fell on top of me. I remember the weight of him." She looked around. The shot that killed her father could have come from the end of the second row or from the back.

She reached to Mills. "Let me see the photos."

Mills handed the folder to her. "ME's office had one of the first digital cameras ever. The pictures are pretty good."

They were. Sam felt her gorge rise. She breathed deeply and sent her grief to the corner of her mind. She saw a woman crumpled on the ground who might have been her mother. The dais looked like a massacre, more bodies than she could count, including her brother and her father ...

"My dad is lying on his back, Andy."

"What? Let me see that." He stood behind her.

"He fell face down on top of me," Sam said. "Someone must have rolled him over to get me out."

"You were pulled to safety," Mills observed. "Maybe staff, or one of the male guests?"

She tried to bring up the painful scene. One minute, she was lying under her dead father, her head turned away from his lifeless eyes. The next minute, she was being pulled out from underneath by a pair of strong arms. Someone was telling her she was safe, a voice she didn't recognize. A man whose brown suit was stained with blood.

Chapter 21

Sam left Detective Sergeant Mills and headed into heavy traffic she scarcely noticed. She followed the GPS directions with a part of her mind and let the rest analyze what she'd just learned. Or what she hadn't learned.

Shell casings pointed to a shooter to the right of the podium and a couple of rows back had gotten off most, if not all the shots. Arthur Randolph. The report confirmed forty-five shots, fourteen of which hit a target. One-third seemed like a high percentage for an inexperienced shooter. Randolph had engaged in recreational shooting as a boy, so he wasn't a complete novice.

Both she and the best man had seen the man in the brown suit, and both had seen the gun. Who brings a gun to a wedding? An assassin or maybe a bodyguard. Would her father have hired someone to protect the guests? If so, the guy had failed. He got his gun out, but he didn't manage to stop the shooting.

She suddenly needed to talk with Terry. She punched in his number and held her breath. When he answered on the second ring, she could feel the tension in the back of her neck ease.

"Hey, Tate, you caught me between the supervisor me and the student me."

"Guess that means I get plain old you. How's your day been?"

"The usual. Saving civilization by day, studying my ass off at night. We've got a serial killer running around Wyoming, of all places. Some new players are taking the place of the drug runners we shut down in Florida last year. One of my field agents quit. On the other hand, I got an A on an important paper."

"Way to bury the story," she exclaimed. "Congratulations."

"It all helps," he said. "So, how's it going for you? Where are you, by the way? In a car?"

"Yes. It's been a long day."

"Do you have time to tell me?"

"Given the volume of traffic on 495, I do. Bright and early, I walked into Manhattan South, where Ron Zielinski immediately offered me a consulting contract. Part-time, one week at a time, stipend."

"That's great," Terry replied. "Wait, isn't it?"

"Depends on whether you believe someone can go from liability to asset in the space of a few days."

"I've seen it happen," Terry said. "Did you accept?"

"I did."

"For what it's worth, I think you did the right thing. Your work is acknowledged, you have a degree of protection as an NYPD adjunct, and you can shorten your vacation by a couple of days if it's not working out. You could check with Tanner, although I assume what you do with your own time is your business. Definitely forget about the role of politics in all this."

"Pretty much what Lopez said."

"I like her. What else?"

"I worked online alongside a smart young tech officer and a couple of detectives, one who likes me and one who doesn't, to gather info on our chat room participants."

Terry grunted. "First of all, hard to believe anyone doesn't like you. Second, I won't ask you how you got information on anonymous people chatting on a website."

"Same way your agency does," she retorted.

He guffawed. "Got me there. Did you get any good leads?"

"More like persons of interest."

"Sounds productive. None of that should put you on 495 during rush hour, though."

Of course he'd more than caught up. Terry was the best investigator she knew.

"I'm on my way back from meeting an almost retired detective at Antun's. He was able to bring along a lot of information and photos and such about the wedding shooting."

"My God, Sam. That must have been hard."

"It was confusing," she admitted. "I didn't learn much that was new. Nothing that confirms a second gunman. Doesn't mean someone wasn't there with a gun. Two of us remember that much. If so, why didn't he shoot? Unless he did, and then he scooped up all the casings. None of which sheds much light on the person who apparently lifted me out from under my father's body, either while Randolph was shooting or soon after. Because I seem to remember a brown suit."

"Are you thinking that your second gunman was not a bad guy but a good guy?"

"I don't know anymore, Terry. If I don't remember being taken off that platform, I can't be certain about anything else, can I?"

"Sam ..."

"Maybe the problem is I have too much Quinn on the brain. Or should I say, Sean Parker."

"Speaking of which—"

His offhanded tone was at odds with the Terry Sloan she knew.

"Uh-oh." She forced a lightness into her voice she didn't feel. "Should I pull over?"

"Senator Sean Parker called me."

"He what?" Her mind scrambled to find a plausible explanation. "Oh, you mean someone from his office called. Or someone attached to the committee he sits on, Homeland Security and Governmental Affairs."

"Nope. The man himself."

"What did he want?" Her whole body was headed into a clench.

"Relax, Sam. He simply wanted to discuss your, what did he call it, 'professional trajectory.' I think he meant your career path."

"Why you? Why now?"

"Why not? He is the senator from Maryland, and you have been in the news. Odds are, he's familiar with your work in Talbot County and most recently with the NYPD. Maybe he has another job in mind for you. Sam? You still there?"

"I wonder if he was the influential someone who changed NYPD minds about me," she said slowly.

"You think Parker stepped in to make sure you stayed on the case?" Terry sounded incredulous. "Why would he do that?"

"To keep me occupied. To stop me from looking into my past."

Silence.

"You don't agree." Disappointment covered her like a blanket.

"Let's lay it out, Tate. We can connect the man who appeared in your old neighborhood to the man who showed up at your brother's wedding. The best man says the brown-suited guy he saw called himself Quinn. Is it the same Quinn as your mother's half-brother? Maybe. Is that person Sean Parker? I don't know."

"The eyes—"

"Are green like yours. Only two percent of the world's population has green eyes but that's still a hundred and fifty-six million people."

She had to laugh. "How do you know that?"

"I looked it up to use in a discussion with you." He paused. "Sam, here's an idea. Once you finish with your crime-solving vacation, take a few extra days to go meet with the senator. He's been calling around about you; I'm sure he'll give you the time. Find out what he wants. That may give you some insight as to who he is. Sometimes direct is best."

"I'll think about it."

She hung up, turning over the conversation in her mind.

The ride back took longer than expected. Sam arrived back at the small house at 5 p.m. to a note from Rosa about an early dinner with friends and leftovers in the refrigerator. The woman certainly had a full social calendar. Or was she keeping herself busy in order not to burden her busy niece?

The very notion filled Sam with remorse. Why couldn't she stop chasing ghosts, not to mention serial killers, and spend more time with the relative she'd waited too long to visit?

She poured herself a generous glass of wine and immediately poured it back into the bottle. She didn't need alcohol or even food; she needed a nap. Just twenty minutes, she promised herself. Then she lay down and fell asleep for over an hour.

Chapter 22

She shot out of bed, astonished that her body had taken command of her brain so easily. She was at least refreshed, if not rested.

She retrieved her rugged backpack out of the closet. With its double-stitched compartments, heavy duty zippers and utility-style cord pulls, it was a dependable travel companion, roomy and lightweight.

She took a laundry list of supplies: wallet, hairbrush, a pair of reading glasses she hated but needed, energy bar, Mag flashlight, utility knife, gloves, zip ties, scarf, water-resistant windbreaker, phone, and keys. Her gun, badge, and critical ID went into a belly bag that fit under her clothes. Running shoes, nylon pants, and a hoodie, all black, completed the ensemble.

Just your friendly female cat burglar.

She'd left her car on the street with the NYPD dashboard ID Zielinski had loaned her. She wasn't sure how that would square with her Maryland plates. Thankfully, the vehicle was still there, intact and unticketed. She breathed a sigh of relief, plugged directions into her navigation system, and headed south.

Traffic was light and she arrived in plenty of time for the seven thirty meeting time. She texted:

here

and waited. Almost immediately, she received directions to a self-storage facility just beyond the glitzy building where they'd met with Theo Austin less than a week earlier.

Sam parked along the main thoroughfare and walked over to a large warehouse that had been repurposed to accommodate differing storage needs. While the block was reasonably well-lit, it was empty save for a single van driving away. The facility itself looked closed, but she guessed the rental perks entailed twenty-four-hour access as well as video security.

The building's entryway was flanked by two full-size bays clearly meant for the largest items. Successful storage places offered a variety of units so that customers could store anything from a couple of boxes to a boat.

A second text came in with more instructions and access codes for the front door and the elevator. The overhead camera winked. Someone was watching, for better or worse.

Sam punched in the numbers on a keypad and entered a simple but cheerfully painted area that likely served as a customer service check-in during business hours. Directly ahead of her stood a high counter with a monitor, a phone, and a stand that held brochures. A couple of chairs sat against one wall. An Industry City calendar hung next to several shelves lined with boxes of trash bags and gloves, along with an array of locks for sale. The elevator was to the right of the display, and stairs were next to that. The main fixtures were turned off, but discreet inset lighting provided adequate illumination.

In the elevator, she entered a second set of numbers and rode to the third floor. Lights went on as she stepped out, which suggested the floor was empty of people. Once again, she wondered about the lack of activity. It was seven thirty, not midnight. In a city like

New York, someone had to be checking on their possessions.

The corridor that included unit 3507 wasn't hard to find, thanks to the signage along the passageways. Based on the size of the bright-blue steel doors, she figured the units in this section to be perhaps 5 x 7 feet, enough room to store several boxes, a bike, and maybe a chair. Where was she supposed to meet brains&beauty, a.k.a. Teresa Albon? In front of the unit? Inside? The texts didn't provide her with any clues.

She stuck the phone in her back pocket and peered down the row. Each of the units had a padlock; 3507 did not. In fact, the door was open.

Sam pulled her gun, took a few steps back, and glanced down the adjacent corridors. Empty. She noted the security cameras at the far corners, red lights blinking. She inched toward her destination. A quick check indicated no lights on these cameras. Malfunctioning or shut down.

Maybe no one was watching her. Maybe Teresa was inside, the padlock in her pocket. Sam preferred those thoughts to any alternatives. She pressed her back against the wall, gripped her gun with both hands, steadied her breathing.

And go! she ordered herself and jumped in front of the unit.

The interior was nearly empty, save for a single overhead light, a canister, and an ice chest. And a small pile of clothes crumpled on the floor. No, a small body, capped by short red-gold hair. Teresa Albon, a.k.a. Theo Austin.

Sam rushed over and felt for a pulse. Still there. Gently, she turned over the woman and yelped as her fingers encountered a piece of dry ice. Austin had burns around her mouth. Her jaw was swollen but not visibly busted. The abdomen wasn't distended, either. All good signs, but Sam wasn't a doctor. She needed to get the woman to safety.

She glanced around, trying to assess the immediate danger. The chest likely held remnants of dry ice. The canister concerned her more. She detected a faint hissing sound. The container could be connected to a timer slowly releasing concentrated carbon dioxide into the unit. She had to get Austin out, so she could—

The crash caught her off guard. Too late, she realized the opening had been propped up by a thick wooden beam that now lay on the floor. The unencumbered steel fell hard and fast. Sam shoved her backpack underneath. The bag's aluminum frame folded in on itself yet held the door an inch and a half above the floor.

She fell back, gasping. Too late, she took in the disabled mechanisms: the missing springs, the sheared off inner handle, the metal rod jammed into the counterbalance. The wooden beam had been nothing more than a primitive but effective trap, easily kicked out of the way. Which meant they weren't alone.

A pair of gloved hands reached down to jerk the backpack free. Sam dropped flat, stuck her gun barrel under the door, aimed for a sneakered foot, and fired. She had the satisfaction of hearing the owner of that foot emit a high-pitched scream and stumble just out of view.

The short period of yelling that followed might have been made by a man or a woman; Sam couldn't be sure. Whoever it was, she'd caused serious injury judging by the blood-slickened floor. She scuttled away from the opening in case whoever she injured decided to return the favor and shoot back.

The bellowing morphed into a sustained moan, followed by the sound of cloth ripping. The distressed assailant was angry but also busy. After a couple of minutes, she heard a grunt and a shuffling sound. The feet reappeared, one clumsily bandaged in what seemed to be a T-shirt. The injured figure made another half-hearted attempt to pull out the backpack from underneath the door, then pivoted to the elevator. The feet moved out of view. She heard the elevator door open and close.

She risked a quick peek and saw a trail of blood leading to the exit. She and Austin were alone in a windowless room with what was undoubtedly a slow-leaking cannister of CO2. She pulled her phone from her pocket. No bars.

Sam crawled over to Austin, lifted the woman under the armpits, pulled her to the unit entrance, and lay her down so her head faced the slivered opening. Better access to oxygenated air might slow the effects of the dry ice.

Next, she took off her jacket and went to wrap up the cannister, taking care not to touch it. She had no idea if that would inhibit the release of the poison, but she had to try.

She used her phone's flashlight to examine the entryway. Not only had the springs been removed, but the chain hoist was gone. Maybe she could repurpose the timber that had been used as a prop. She needed to lift the door high enough to get the wood underneath. That would give her six inches.

She squatted close to the door and shoved her toes underneath as far as they would go. She couldn't have pulled them out if she wanted to, and she really wanted to. She couldn't squat without turning her knees out as far as they could go. Her positioning couldn't have been worse. She might strain her meniscus, injure her hip flexor, or tear her ACL.

She inhaled the polluted air and heaved. Her neck and shoulder muscles protested. The door moved four inches. Not enough. She let go with a curse and almost crushed her toes.

On the second attempt, accompanied by more vocalization, she got an additional five inches. She let go as she kicked the beam in position as a support. It shuddered under the falling steel but held.

Exhausted, she sat on the ground, head in hands. From her head to her wounded toes, her body rebelled.

I can't do any more, a little voice told her.

She glanced at the canister, then at the prone figure lying to her left. "Yes, you can," she said aloud.

She squatted again, pushed her feet all the way under the gate, placed her hands to either side. She lifted with everything she had: her pain, her fury, and her determination accompanied by the soundtrack of her warrior cry.

The door flew up and immediately began to fall, lured by gravity and its own weight.

She dove for the bulky beam and hoisted it up to a vertical position to catch the door about a third of the way down. The wood held, but the precarious angle made it wobbly. She kicked her backpack into the corridor and pulled Austin to safety just as the timber collapsed and the steel door hit the concrete floor with a thunderous crash.

"Way to cut it close, Tate," she panted. She grabbed her pack, lifted Theo Austin in her arms, and stood. The pain, held at bay by a combination of endorphins and sheer will, began to sneak its way back into her consciousness. She staggered to the elevator, reached the first floor, and propelled herself out the front door and into Margarite Lopez.

Chapter 23

"Teresa Albon. Theo Austin. Dry ice. Hospital." Sam spat out the words and began to sink. Lopez caught her and Austin with both arms. Zielinski materialized and took the tiny woman from Sam as if she were a fragile package. Carlisle emerged from the shadows, cell phone in hand, Nichols beside him.

"Ambulance will be here in five," Carlisle reported. "I got in a call to DOH, just in case."

"You'll need them," Sam gasped.

"Are you having trouble breathing?" Lopez asked. "Or standing? What the hell happened to your boots?"

Sam felt herself deflating as the adrenaline rush subsided and exhaustion set in. She lifted her head and filled her lungs with air. Oxygen had never seemed so appealing.

"Can you get me over to the car?" she asked. "If I sit down here, I won't get up." Her arms and legs felt like jelly and her feet ached. "By the way, how did you know I was here?"

"You're not a good liar, Tate," Lopez said. "I knew Albon sent you specifics of a meetup. I had Jessica track your phone's GPS. Credit to her for figuring out Albon was really Austin, by the way."

"I should have figured it out."

"Holden's mind works in a particular way. I'll explain it after we get you in a seated position."

Lopez and Carlisle got her halfway into the back seat. They leaned in as she gave them a brief overview of her activities, Nichols just behind.

"I don't even know what time it is," she said.

"Eight forty-five," Lopez said.

"Let me get this straight," Carlisle said. "You shot the attacker in the foot through a one-inch opening, then deadlifted a broken steel door, using a wooden beam for leverage, all while breathing CO_2?"

"Don't forget she carried Austin out of the building on those feet of hers," Lopez added.

Sam looked around. "I'm almost certain the attacker left a blood trail. Make sure someone collects a sample."

"We'll have our people process the scene," Carlisle told her.

"He couldn't have gotten very far."

"You know it was a male?" Lopez asked.

"Yes," Sam nodded. The movement caused her to wince.

"Okay, let me get on this," Lopez said. "Danny, make sure she's treated."

Lopez walked off, leaving Sam with a clear view of Chloe Nichols, arms folded across her chest. Irritation pulled at the corners of her mouth. Sam would have laughed if she weren't certain it would hurt. Poor Detective Nichols. She probably didn't appreciate being pulled away from her evening routine. She certainly didn't like the way Lopez and Carlisle were fawning over Sam. She likely resented all the fuss being made over an outsider who went rogue. Maybe she'd complain.

An ambulance screeched into view. The paramedics took Austin from Zielinski and got her onto a stretcher and fitted with an oxygen mask. He exchanged a few words with one of the EMTs, who then grabbed a knapsack and followed the detective back to the group.

Sure enough, Nichols waylaid Zielinski and began talking in low, urgent tones. Before she'd gotten very far, he held up a hand. Sam distinctly heard him say, “We’re not going to talk about this now.”

“You’re going to the hospital,” Carlisle told Sam.

“Don’t need to. The medics can check me out here.”

Lopez stood up as a second pair of flashing lights appeared. “Precinct cops have arrived. How about I go fill them in?” She trotted off.

The impossibly young paramedic squatted by the car and started to unpack his gear. “Good evening, Officer,” he said to Sam. “I assume you were in the room with the CO2 as well.”

“That’s not all,” Carlisle replied. He went down the list of Sam’s various exploits. Sam could see him struggle not to laugh as the paramedic’s eyes began to bug.

“You really need to go to the hospital,” the young man insisted when the detective had finished.

“The woman I brought out, she’s the one who needs to get to the hospital,” Sam began just as the youthful EMT slid a mask over her face.

“We’re going to give you a hit of oxygen first thing while we check out the rest of you, including those feet.”

“But ...”

“Breathe slowly and deeply,” he ordered. “The woman you rescued is getting the treatment she needs. Trust me, we know what we’re doing. If she needs to go before I’m done with you, the medics will make sure she goes. My name is Pat Riley, by the way.”

He began with a flashlight in Sam’s eyes and instructions about following his finger. “No concussion. Excellent.”

Sam moved her mask. “I didn’t knock my head,” she protested.

"Noted. Keep the mask on, please, while I check the rest of you."

He moved to Sam's neck and shoulders. Poking, kneading, moving her head. She flinched but was generally relieved to find things seemed to be in working order.

"No apparent broken bones, nothing seems to have popped or ruptured, thank God," Riley pronounced. "Definite muscle and tendon strain. How much does a steel door weigh?"

"Let's see, says here two hundred and fifty pounds," Carlisle replied, holding up his phone.

Riley whistled. "Impressive, Detective. You obviously used your technique to good advantage."

Carlisle grinned.

The medic pressed her stomach region carefully. "I have no way of knowing if you have internal bleeding without a scan," he said. "The good news is I have a portable machine, so we'll do that here after I finish the preliminary exam."

Next, the medic checked her hips and knees. "You may have strained the hip flexor. The lay term is groin pull. That'll hurt tomorrow. You've got some swelling around the kneecaps. But you're wincing, not screaming, which is a good sign."

He moved down to her boots. "And what happened here?"

"I jammed my feet under the door to get some leverage. I'm afraid my first lift wasn't all that successful."

Riley stared at Sam to see if she was teasing him. "Okay," he said when he realized she wasn't. "That's definitely not good technique." He looked more carefully.

"Your boots held up fairly well, all things considered. I'll have to get them off to see if the same can be said about your feet. It could hurt quite a bit. We could find something to cut them off if you prefer. You're not going to wear them again."

"I prefer we get this over with and you get Theo to the hospital. Just yank them off."

The paramedic did as he was told and was rewarded with a vigorous "Shit!"

Both feet were swollen, the right far more than the left. The tops were so bruised they appeared blackened. Riley pushed gently while Sam bit her lip to keep from crying out.

"The good news is, nothing seems torn or broken," he told Sam. "No punctures or cuts, and, as you can see, no external bleeding. Your feet are, however, severely bruised. The skin at the top of the foot is very thin, so this is to be expected. The bruises don't extend to the sole, although I suspect you'll have some muscle cramping. The third toe on your right foot may be sprained."

He looked at her. "They will heal, providing you take care of them. This is not a joke. Tissue injuries can cause problems. Stay off your feet for a few days. No boots or tie shoes for at least ten days. Use slippers or sandals with socks if necessary. Keep your feet iced all day tomorrow until you can't stand it. I'm going to give you a tube of Arnica for the bruises, a prescription for extra-strength Tylenol, a short course of antibiotics just in case, and a couple of Valium."

He handed her a bottle of water. "I'm going to give you one of the Valium to take now. You'll need it once the shock wears off and your muscles realize what you made them do."

Sam took off her mask and took the pill without complaint.

"Get checked out at a clinic or a hospital tomorrow," the paramedic continued. "And you have to rest, Detective. I'm not kidding. Make sure someone's with you this evening. Expect to feel awful tomorrow. Don't try to work through the pain."

"Promise."

He gave her a pulse ox test. "Ninety-seven percent," he crowed. "Impressive. Okay, we're off."

"Wait." Sam laid a hand on the young man's arm. "First of all, thank you. Second, can you tell me how the other woman is doing?"

"You'll need to check in with the hospital. She's alive, thanks to you."

Several more vehicles arrived. The DOH van dislodged a suited-up hazmat team. A gray-haired man conversed briefly with the occupant of a dark-blue sedan with the storage company logo on the side. Sam guessed he was the building's manager or owner. The guy was going to be dealing with his own headaches.

Nichols was taking a call. "CO says to check in when you're done here," she said to Carlisle.

"Figures," Carlisle replied with a smile. "First, we need to take care of Sam. Last chance: Hospital or no?"

Sam shook her head.

"Where's your car?" Carlisle asked.

"Second Avenue. Keys are in the front compartment." She handed him the crumbled backpack.

"Stay out of the main section and you'll avoid any broken glass. Easy does it, though. That's my favorite carry-on."

"I doubt you'll be carrying it again," Nichols said.

"Zipper still works," Carlisle said. "Impressive. Ah, success." He dangled the key ring. "However, you're not driving."

"I can get her home," Nichols offered.

Sam thought she'd rather walk.

"You know what would help, Chloe?" Zielinski said. "Maybe you can locate Lopez. We're going to need to stick around. Danny can get her home and come right back."

Nichols turned on her heel and marched off.

"She's a little grumpy," Carlisle observed.

"I don't really care," Sam replied. "But I have to get in touch with Rosa." She reached for her phone, safe in her back pocket. "My poor aunt. I come for a visit and upend her life."

"Stay at my place," Carlisle said suddenly. "I have a guest bedroom that's very comfortable and surprisingly quiet."

"Danny, I couldn't ..." She spoke slowly. When did her tongue get so thick?

"Can't what, Tate?" Lopez reappeared, along with Nichols and a heavyset man with thick eyebrows that sat on his face like a permanent scowl.

The perfect match for Nichols, Sam thought.

"This is Detective Sergeant Steve Cairn," Lopez said. "This area is in his precinct. I filled him in as to how and why we preceded him on the scene."

The man gave a curt nod. "We've got our people patrolling the area," he began. "The assailant left a blood trail near the storage unit, but it ends in the elevator. I can't say for certain where he exited the building, assuming he did. We'll make sure he's not still inside, don't worry. By the way, seems like your killer is trying to hit all the boroughs. Maybe you can give the local precincts in Staten Island a heads-up when he moves over there." He didn't smile.

"Brooklyn Homicide is aware of the Dry Ice Killer case, Detective Sergeant," Carlisle replied. "We're not trying to cut anyone out."

"Fortunately, we're all on the same side," Lopez said. "Which means we all want to stop this SOB before he tries anything else in any borough."

Zielinski joined them. "Theo Austin is on the way to the hospital. I'm going to follow along and see when she can give us a statement. Detective Sergeant Cairn, perhaps you'd like to join me?"

Cairn appeared briefly mollified. "Thanks. I'll catch up with you. We have other problems right here, including a potentially contaminated floor, if not the whole structure, that has to be treated before forensics can do their thing. Hazmat may have to enter other units, which requires an okay from someone or several someones. The third floor may remain inaccessible to the renters for a while. I don't envy the building manager." He walked away.

"We're going to want to review whatever security footage is available," Zielinski said.

"Cameras were out near our unit," Sam managed to say.

"Well, let's check the others."

"Chloe and I will help," Carlisle said. "As soon as I get Sam settled." He got an arm around her waist and helped her stand.

"She needs to rest, Danny," Lopez said sharply.

"And she will, Margarite," Carlisle retorted.

He helped Sam over to her car, tucked her into the passenger seat, and fastened the seat belt. For good measure, he put his jacket over her, which earned him a smile and a sigh.

"I can tell the Valium is working," he said. "Sam, we're going to my place. I'm not going to scare your poor aunt by dumping you at her doorstep in your condition. I have a neighbor I can ask to look in on you until I get back. Okay? Contact Rosa; tell her you're on a case."

"I'll let her know," Sam replied. All she wanted to do was sleep. She sent her aunt a text about pulling an all-nighter with the squad and hoped that made her seem as if she were somewhere safe, surrounded by competent, trained professionals. Better than letting Rosa know she decided to head solo into a darkened warehouse to meet a mysterious contact with information on a homicidal maniac—who then turned up and tried to kill them both.

Will check in tomorrow, she added. Exhausted by the effort, she dropped the phone onto the center console and lay her head back.

She really did feel safe, in the car with the more than competent and oh-so handsome Detective Danny Carlisle. Safe and warm under his jacket, driving through the city, the hundreds of lights twinkling like stars ...

Chapter 24

The shaft of sunlight hit Sam squarely in the face. She blinked twice, bolted upright, and immediately regretted the effort. Every bone in her body ached, every muscle cried for mercy. She felt like someone had stuffed her mouth with cotton and thrown her down a flight of stairs. Repeatedly.

As painful as it was to be awake, the condition was preferable to the most recent dream state in which a monstrous machine was crushing the life out of her. She recalled a green-eyed man but couldn't tell if he was trying to kill her or save her.

Awake now, she took in the completely unfamiliar surroundings. She was in a modern bedroom decorated in soothing tones of gray and cream. An abstract painting on one wall presented as a forest below a cerulean sky. The blond wood furniture with its clean lines and simple design, managed to be both functional and appealing. The fixtures might have been sculpted. Several pillows in deep teal were piled at the end of her bed.

She threw back the coverlet and eased her legs over the side of the mattress. The movement hurt every bit as much as sitting up in bed. And her feet! More puce than purple. Rust-colored in spots and yellow in others. Swollen and not only on top. She couldn't have put on shoes if she'd wanted to.

She stood and cried out. *Breathe through the pain,* she told herself. She gritted her teeth and limped to the window. The slatted shades rose at a touch to open onto a view of sparkling water fronting a panorama that was the Manhattan skyline. A ferry boat moved leisurely across the serene river. Trees of red, orange, and gold dotted the waterfront park. She was facing west; the sun had cleared the building. A little past noon, she guessed, an observation confirmed by the transparent analog clock on the wall that read 12:20.

She was in Danny Carlisle's apartment in Long Island City. Wearing a sort of oversized flannel shirt that must have been his. Underpants, no bra. Her black denim jeans and jacket were folded on the chair near the dresser, along with an unfamiliar pair of sandals, socks, and a pale blue T-shirt that looked to be her size.

Sam went back to the bed and plopped down, willing her sluggish mind to remember something, anything. She wasn't in a guest bedroom; the aesthetic of the space, along with a few details, suggested she'd slept in the master suite. In his room. She didn't see a dent in the far side of the queen bed. Where had he slept?

Her eyes went to her phone, patiently vibrating on the nightstand. Next to it was a note, handwritten in a sort of reverse scrawl. Was he left-handed? Had she realized that?

Decided to let you sleep in. You needed it. Coffee is ready to go, bagels and fruit are on the counter. Take your pills with food. The shoes and shirt are on loan from Fran (neighbor) since yours are trashed. You can leave the keys with her. BTW, Fran changed you out of your clothes. Also, she's fifty-eight and married. Call your aunt. Then call me.

She stayed where she was to give herself time to absorb the information. Danny had brought her back to his apartment. He'd persuaded a female neighbor named Fran to help. He'd slept somewhere else, checked up on her, and left her coffee and bagels.

The idea of falling all the way back into bed and pulling the covers over her head appealed to her. Nevertheless, she dragged herself into a small kitchen with first-class appliances and an island that divided it from a living room with more breathtaking views. If this apartment was rent-controlled, Danny Carlisle was the luckiest man in the five boroughs.

Hunger suddenly took over, a good sign as far as she was concerned. Half a bagel with cream cheese, half an apple, and two cups of coffee later, she felt almost human, albeit a compromised one.

Rosa answered the phone on the first ring. "There you are," she said cheerily. "Your nice friend called and told me everyone was working very hard. Are you getting enough to eat? You must be exhausted. Will you be home tonight?"

Though her aunt was trying for nonchalant, Sam could tell she'd been worried sick.

"I'm fine, Rosa, but yes, tired. We're eating, but nothing beats your home cooking." She suspected she had coaxed a small smile out of her aunt. "I'll be home for dinner by six, followed by an early bedtime."

Sam disconnected, took her coffee, and stood in front of one of the floor-to-ceiling windows. She guessed they were about thirty-five floors up, enough to gain a wide vista, but still low enough to see some details in the green park below. For a minute, she breathed as deeply as her battered body permitted and tried to imagine coming home to this view every day.

With a shake of her head, Sam brought herself back to the present. She could have died last night. Theo almost did. She really wanted to nail the son of a bitch responsible.

She went back to the kitchen island, perched on a stool, and called Carlisle.

"How are you?" he asked. "Did you sleep okay?"

"Better than I expected to. Um, did you? Get any sleep, I mean?" She felt like an idiot for asking, even more so when he laughed.

"Hang on a minute," he said. She heard footsteps echoing down what must have been a hallway. "Okay, I have a little more privacy now. About last night. You were in pretty bad shape. I put you in my bed, as you probably noticed."

"I know, Danny, and I really appreciate—"

"I slept in the guest bedroom," he said quickly. "Fran changed you. Not that I wouldn't have been happy to do the honors under other circumstances, but it wasn't the right time, and I would never—"

It was Sam's turn to laugh, and she did so, gratefully. "Danny, honestly, it's fine. You were dealing with a woman who was zonked out in more ways than one. You acted like a human being. More than that. Like a good friend."

"Okay, then." He exhaled.

"When did you get in?"

"About four this morning." He yawned.

"Where are you now?"

"I'm at Maimonides Medical Center, which is where they took Theo Austin last night. It's a trauma one hospital center, which is good. Her injuries are unusual."

"How is she doing?"

"First, the good news. The CO2 has been flushed out of her system and the doctor reports no internal organ damage. Her jaw is badly bruised, and she's got a couple of broken teeth. Her tongue and throat sustained cold burns, as did her hands."

"What's the bad news?"

"Right now, she can't talk. Her throat injuries might require surgery. She's being monitored for infection. The pain is probably through the roof. Doctors have her on a cocktail that includes a light sedative to keep her in twilight."

"How long before they know what they need to do?"

"Could be twenty-four hours."

"I ought to get over there."

"There's nothing to be done. In fact, I'm headed into the Manhattan Precinct to meet with Zielinski."

"I guess poor Theo is certainly off the person of interest list. Can't imagine her trying to poison herself, especially like that. But she might know something. Hey, did anything come of your meeting with Tom Levy yesterday?"

"Not really. Levy's a smart man. He already figured we might ask about his son's case. Said his son's murder had gained a lot more attention than others might get. He understood our focus on victims' families with grievances, but he felt there might be another motive at play. Not that he could tell us what that motive was or why he felt that way."

Sam pointed her toes and almost yelped. She pulled her foot back. "What does Tasha say about all this?" she asked. "As a former cop, she's gotta have an opinion about what's going on."

"Apparently, she's unreachable. Levy saw her Saturday afternoon for a taping. She might have mentioned something about going off the grid. She's due in this afternoon. Lopez and Nichols are going to visit the rest of your potentials today.

"I can grab a cab and join them." She stood, gasped, and sat back down.

"Not a chance. What you can do is take a hot shower and slather that arnica jell on your feet. Which probably look and feel like crap."

"They aren't pretty," she admitted. "But Danny, I can't sit around and do nothing!"

"Maybe you can sit around and do something. Levy thinks there are likely to be clues in the DFD transcripts. I think he's onto something. Assuming our killer has been active for at least a month, we need to zero in on some of the interactions between our people of interest and our three victims."

"What if the killer was lurking? What if he or she never said anything?"

"I'm not the serial killer expert, but I think our guy or gal craves attention. The killings are macabre but also showy. I suspect the murderer can't resist speaking up."

"You're not wrong."

"That's what I like to hear. I'll have Holder send everything over. You can use my laptop in the den. Obviously, your phone works. Call if you need anything. I gotta go. Take the pills, take the shower, call Holder. Check you later."

Chapter 25

The contents of Sam's backpack had been placed on the dining room table. Everything was in surprisingly good condition: wallet, credit cards, even the cash. The glasses and flashlight were broken. The list she'd made at the beginning of the case—was it really only a week ago? —remained intact, tucked inside the wallet.

She took the crumbled paper into the office. The space doubled as a guest bedroom, judging by the sheets and blankets neatly folded and stacked at the corner of the couch. She peeked into the adjoining bathroom and saw a toothbrush. The sight made her feel better.

The place was tidied up; Carlisle had even left a bottle of water by the computer, along with the passwords needed. She logged in and saw that Holder had wasted no time in sending over transcripts for eight chats going back five weeks. Despite her tremendous discomfort, Sam was glad to have something to do.

She had intended to highlight comments from her three victims and five detectives. Instead, she decided to read the transcripts as a whole and annotate as she went along.

Two hours later, she sat back and stretched. She had a page full of notes but no idea how much she'd learned.

While most of the DFDs projected confidence, bythebook came across more self-effacing. Stephanie Chen probably knew more about most topics than the average person. Sam couldn't tell if her on-screen demeanor was put on or simply a habit reinforced by cultural expectations. Soulsaver, a.k.a. Father Clemons, was similarly disposed to modesty, frequently assuming the role of mediator. As for actingcyclist, Grant Paulson approached the chats as a creative exercise. His suggestions were at times fanciful but never malicious. He took the predictable ribbing with good nature.

Those were the victims. The larger group of detectives was a varied lot. Wknddad tended to be officious. Deepdiver was, well, shallow. Both notmydayjob and seenitall made a point of flaunting their abilities. Dedicateddetective and brains&beauty had their prickly moments. Strongcoffee had strong opinions. Workingmom was cheerful but displayed flashes of irritation, and renaissancewoman was either fretful or flaky.

The others were more tempered in their contributions and seemed as if they might be interesting people with interesting lives outside their shared fascination with true crime. She wouldn't mind having coffee with the physicist or the mystery writer.

She went back to her original list to see how much more she could add. Despite efforts to chronicle and catalog deviant behavior, killers were rarely one thing or another. The same held true of their motives. Someone seeking revenge might also enjoy torture. Someone seeking justice might also want to be admired or respected for their work.

Respect. Sam had seen that word crop up in the discussion more than a few times. It was an odd word in the context of discussing a cold case, wasn't it? More the kind of thing you'd hear at a self-help meeting or a relationship seminar.

Before she could put more thought into it, her phone played its latest ringtone. During lockdown, she'd programmed it with a theme from one of the cable news shows that signaled breaking news. Her phone rang so rarely that any call was an event. Now she thought she'd like a day in which it didn't ring or beep or somehow insist she remain alert and ready.

She swallowed her sigh and answered.

"Hey, Lieutenant Tate, it's Jessica Holder. Just checking to see if you're okay and if you have everything you need."

"How would you define respect?"

Holder didn't miss a beat. "I guess I'd say respect is about acknowledgement or recognition. The idea is that the person is seen or heard, right? They're appreciated or their work is appreciated. No one takes them for granted. Like the Aretha Franklin song, right?"

"Yeah, I've already got that earworm rattling around my head. Never mind. You asked if I had what I needed. Yes, thanks. And call me Sam, okay?"

"Okay, Sam." She sounded pleased.

Sam stood. She was stiff, but her feet were marginally less painful.

"Actually, there is something, Jessica. Can you run a background check on Ravi Patel, the *Deep Freeze* audio engineer? It occurs to me we don't know a lot about him."

"Well, he's twenty-eight, he was born in Edison, New Jersey, second oldest of four kids, went to school at Berklee College of Music in Boston, which is a really good school. He came back to New York to try to advance his career as a songwriter; he writes indie pop-fusion music with some Indian influences, and he's working with an experienced lyricist. Anyway, he fell into sound engineering almost by accident, but it pays and he likes it. His position with the podcast takes up most of his time now because of the website."

Sam laughed, which felt better than she expected. "I stand corrected, Jessica. You know a lot about him. Maybe we can just see if he has an alibi for Monday night—"

"He does," Holder jumped in.

"And you know this how?"

"We, um, we had a drink Monday night. Oh, and food. We definitely had food. And another drink."

"So, a date?"

"I don't know if you'd call it that."

"Okay, you had a get-together over food and drink with the guy you thought was, at the very least, negligent about maintaining a website where a killer might be stalking his victims."

"I didn't think of it like that. Am I in trouble?"

Sam smiled to herself. "No, Jessica, you're not. He wasn't really a person of interest, at least not until his name popped into my addled brain. Clearly you see something in him, and I trust your instincts. If you vouch for him, he's not one now. I'm more surprised than anything else."

"He's really funny, Lieutenant—Sam. And smart. We've been talking about ways to safeguard the website. He wants to do better. I told him I'd help, and he suggested we make it an evening. I didn't break any confidences."

"I'm sure you didn't, and I'm sure you won't. Thanks for the information. I'll call you later if I need anything."

The clock in the den said 2:45 p.m. Sam debated putting in a few more hours, but her head hurt. For that matter, so did the rest of her. She pushed herself back into the kitchen, toasted another half bagel, and ate it slowly. She wasn't hungry, but she needed to take her pills. She knew better than to try it on a stomach filled mostly with coffee.

Dressing took time. The clothes were at least soft and loose. Though she hadn't ever imagined going out in socks and sandals, Sam decided the combination would be the most comfortable option. She'd have to put her belongings in a plastic bag, but she doubted a cab driver would care.

She went out on the porch and gazed across the water at the iconic skyline. For a full minute, all she did was listen to the murmured sound of traffic and the buzz of life in the city, to the voices in her head, to the beating of her heart. Then she called Terry, and they talked for almost an hour.

Finally, she called a car service, packed up, set the alarm, and left for the less rarified neighborhood in Queens where her aunt lived.

Chapter 26

"Sam, honey, wake up. I brought you a little breakfast."

Sam sat up with a grunt. She rubbed her eyes against the sunlight that streamed through the handmade lace curtains. She was back in the guest bedroom of her aunt's house. Rosa stood in the doorway with a tray with coffee, a glass of juice, and a muffin so large it spilled over the plate.

"How do you feel, *cara*?" Rosa asked. "You were out like a light."

"How long?" Sam murmured. She carefully rotated her neck, pleased to find the muscles had loosened considerably.

"You went to bed right after dinner. It's eight in the morning. So, thirteen hours." Rosa set the tray on the nightstand. "Your phone has been vibrating like crazy. Eat first, then make your calls."

"Thank you, Aunt Rosa."

As soon as Rosa left, Sam pulled her pills out of the nightstand drawer and took them with a bite of muffin and a glass of water. She pulled her foot from under the covers. The bruises seemed lighter, not quite so colorful. An improvement, she decided.

She reached for her phone. Five texts and two voicemails. Danny, Ron, Margarite, Jessica. She started with Zielinski.

"Sam! How are you feeling?"

"A lot better, thanks." She heard the familiar squawk of a police radio. "Where are you?"

"In Brooklyn. Lopez and Carlisle are on their way."

Sam went on high alert. "Did something happen to Theo?"

"She's fine. I've added more security."

"You're in Brooklyn but not at the hospital?"

"Correct. I'm at a building across from the 84th Precinct that happens to be home to both the Manhattan and Brooklyn Cold Case Squads. Sanitation workers found a body in a dumpster." He choked out the last sentence.

"Someone we know." Sam felt her own throat close.

"Tasha Wright."

"Fuck! Sorry"

"Pretty much what I said. Look, there's more, but I gotta get off and work things out so no one steps on anyone else's toes."

"I'll be there as soon as I can." She'd already pushed herself out of bed. Just a small gasp when the right foot stabbed; the rest was just achy.

"Forget it, Sam. It's rush hour. You're at least forty-five minutes away. We already have more people than we know what to do with. Don't even—"

"Non-negotiable, Ron. See you soon."

She disconnected in the middle of his protest.

Ten minutes later, Sam made her way down the stairs, her bag awkwardly slung over one sore shoulder. Rosa stood at the bottom step with a carafe, a paper bag, and a spacious tawny leather bag.

"Christmas present from the kids," she said, handing her the bag. "Beautiful Italian leather, lightweight, too. Probably cost a fortune. I'll never use it."

"Rosa—"

"You can carry it in the crook of your arm and skip the shoulder altogether. Oh, I noticed your car isn't here, so I called a cab for you," the older woman continued. "I've used Dimitri's service for years. He knows the fastest routes."

As Sam transferred the contents of her old bag to her new one, Rosa pulled a thin black cane from the closet. She glanced at Sam's feet, clad in socks and sandals. "You need to take some weight off that foot," she observed. "I used this after my bunion surgery. It's much stronger than it looks. It's also collapsible. Okay, Dimitri is out front now. Take the coffee and a muffin for the ride. You'll make excellent time. Go."

"I love you," Sam said and hugged her aunt. She gathered her belongings and made her way to the shiny black Cadillac that hovered between old and vintage. A short, stout man with abundant gray hair that didn't quite fit into his watch cap held open the door. Then he zipped around to the driver's side.

"I am Dimitri," he said by way of introduction. "Rosa is my friend. We will go fast, but no small talk, okay? You can eat, but don't drop crumbs and don't leave garbage. Seatbelt please. Also, give me the address."

Sam directed him to the 84th Precinct station. She reasoned the activity would be centered on the area where the body was found. Where Tasha Wright was found.

She swore silently.

Dimitri drove aggressively. He took them on and off the highway and through unfamiliar neighborhoods, muttering to himself and consulting the navigation system on his phone. Sam shoved a piece of muffin into her mouth so she wouldn't yell at him to keep his eyes on the road.

They made excellent time and pulled up to the end of Gold Street not half an hour later. The narrow street was closed to through traffic.

"I can't get any closer," Dimitri said.

"This is fine." She popped on her backup sunglasses and reached into her bag for her wallet.

"No money," he told her. "Rosa and I are good. Leave the mug. I will get it back to her. You need me, call this number." He handed her a crisp business card. "Go."

She pulled herself from the car with a smile and he sped away.

With her provisional NYPD ID on a lanyard, and her Talbot County badge clipped to her belt, Sam passed through the gathering crowd of onlookers and through the temporary barricades, supplemented by a police car with flashing lights and a stern-looking uniformed officer. She worked her way down the narrow street and stopped just short of the tent to text Zielinski.

"Sam! You made it!" Carlisle walked over with his arms outstretched as if he were about to hug her. He settled for a back slap instead. "You look about a million times better."

"Couple days of nonstop sleep and some pills will do that." She smiled. "Along with doting friends and relatives." She lifted the walking stick.

"It means you're prepared. Although maybe not for this. We should have had security on Levy and Wright from the get-go. And anyone of the Deep Freeze Detectives who live in the five boroughs. Damn it!"

"Come on, Danny. I can't imagine Tasha Wright thought she needed any protection." She shook her head. "Where are the others?"

"Zielinski's on his way over to us. Lopez went to break the news to Tom Levy, who will presumably help her with next of kin notification. Chloe is hunting down the precinct detectives who called us."

Sam nodded, looked around. "This is a lot of people, even for NYPD."

"Not for one of their own, Sam. The bastard killed a cop."

"And left her in front of her old workplace," Sam said. "But why?"

Nichols showed up with two detectives, judging by their badges. They seemed a mismatched set. The fair-haired man was well over six feet. His features were small, his shoulders wide, his eyes the color of the Caribbean Sea. Sam estimated the woman at just over five feet, with straight black hair held back by a headband. Watchful sable eyes, grave expression.

"Detective Connie Ito, Brooklyn North Homicide," she said by way of introduction. "This is my partner, Detective Fred Bentley. Detective Nichols has more or less filled us in."

"Detectives Carlisle and Tate," Carlisle said. "We're just waiting for Detective Zielinski from Manhattan South."

"Is he the lead detective on the Dry Ice killings?" Bentley asked.

"That's me," Zielinski replied, hurrying over. "We gotta figure out why our killer is escalating."

"Feeling the pressure," Carlisle suggested. "Trying to finish the mission."

"Or the experiment," Sam said. That earned her a piercing look from Bentley.

"Tate here has some familiarity with serials," Zielinski explained. "Which unfortunately is what we're looking at."

"Sam Tate," Ito said. "I thought I recognized you." She looked as if she was about to say more.

"Have you spoken with Tasha's old colleagues at the Cold Case Squad?" Zielinski asked.

"That's next," Bentley said.

"Can we see the body?" Carlisle asked.

"MLI is almost done," Ito replied. "Let me tell you what we know."

She swung her arm in an arc. "The precinct station is over there, and the Cold Case Squad headquarters is in the building with the scaffolding. The body was found in a dumpster in front of the building. The dumpster is temporary; it's just there while the entrance is being repaired. Garbage is collected by a private company hired by the contractor. Two people came this morning. One noticed an oddly shaped bag, opened it, and fell flat on his ass from the fumes. His partner slammed the dumpster shut and called 9-1-1."

Bentley picked up the story. "DOH sent the hazmat guys because NYPD has been getting calls about homicides involving poisonous gas lately. As soon as DOH determined they were dealing with traces of CO_2, we called you." He pointed at Zielinski, who nodded.

"Good. Can you ask the MLI how much longer?"

"She's probably ready for us," Ito said.

"She?" Bentley asked. "I thought the ME's office sent over a male."

"You have a problem with the fairer sex?" Ito joked.

"No, it's just—" Bentley ran a hand through his crew cut. "Never mind. I need a break and some lousy coffee.

You guys do your thing. I'll be right back." He walked away.

The remaining detectives pulled on disposable gloves and masks, ducked under the canopy and walked over to a fair-skinned light-haired woman in a mask with a digital camera.

"Morning," she said. "I'm Investigator Ginger Baker from the OME's office. Obviously not the famous rock drummer."

Ito made quick introductions. "These are detectives from Manhattan and Queens homicide units. They've been pursuing all leads related to the case they're working on."

"The Dry Ice Killer," Baker replied. "It's all over the news. Objectively speaking, which is all I can do, this woman shares certain postmortem characteristics with the previous victims."

She stepped aside to reveal the body of Tasha Wright. The woman had been brutalized around the face like the other victims. Her jaw appeared broken and several of her teeth were missing. Bloated, her skin mottled, she scarcely resembled the beautiful and vibrant woman Sam met just a week earlier.

She was overtaken by cold fury. This was no way to end a life of service. She put her emotions aside and bent down, puzzled by what she saw.

"Were you able to make a positive ID?" Zielinski asked.

"Her fingertips are burned almost black," the MLI said, "but I was able to pull a partial off the fourth finger of her right hand. She also has a scar around her throat from a previous incident, as noted in her file. Her lips, throat, and tongue have the same kinds of burns. Jaw and several teeth are broken. So is her left wrist, by the way."

"I bet she fought like hell," Carlisle said, his voice tight. "How would the killer have subdued her?"

"Needle to the back of the neck," Baker said. "Could have been an injectable form of a benzodiazepine. And yes, she fought back. I'm hopeful we can get DNA from underneath her fingernails."

"What about cause of death?"

"Distended stomach suggests a rupture, although that may be related to the decomp. I've picked up faint signs of CO2. Very much like your other victims, I understand."

Sam stood. "Not completely," she said. "Tasha didn't die in the last twenty-four hours, did she?"

"No, she didn't," Baker said. "More like seventy-two hours ago, give or take."

"Three days." Sam looked at Carlisle and Zielinski, saw they were thinking the same thing. Tasha Wright had been killed before Theo Austin was attacked.

"Yes, and she was murdered somewhere else and moved, likely within the first twelve hours after her death. The red fibers on her clothes indicate she spent time on some sort of rug or carpet. Can't tell you much else about where she died."

"Thank you, Investigator Baker," Zielinski said. He turned to Carlisle. "Text Lopez. I want a forensics team at the studio ASAP to scour the scene and collect carpet samples."

Carlisle nodded. "You think she was killed at the studio?"

"Let's just say it's a possible crime scene. But Margarite shouldn't let Levy out of her sight."

Sam glanced over at Nichols. The young detective hadn't said a word during the exam. Her notepad was nowhere in sight. Her face was pale, her mouth tight. A slight sheen covered her forehead. She looked sick. Surely this wasn't her first encounter with a corpse? It could be the first time she was seeing someone in death she'd just met in life.

"Chloe? Detective Nichols? You okay?"

"I ... I just need a minute." Nichols backed out of the tent and vanished into the scrum of people.

Sam and Zielinski traded looks.

Bentley met them as they exited the makeshift tent. "Did you get what you need?" he asked.

"For now," Zielinski answered. "The three-day TOD presents certain complications."

"Three days?" Bentley looked at Ito. "That's not what the first guy said."

"What are you talking about, Fred?" Ito asked. "What guy?"

"I arrived here before you, Connie. The MLI on scene was a man. I told him more detectives were expected and asked him to hang around a little. He said he'd actually been called to another scene and a woman was coming in to finish up."

"You ever know it to work that way, Fred?"

"No ..."

"What did this guy look like?" Carlisle demanded.

Bentley shrugged. "Dark hair, thick beard, glasses. Not sure about his eyes."

"Did you get a name?" Sam asked.

The big man shook his head. "He was gone like a shot. Moved fast for a guy with a bad limp."

Chapter 27

[Transcript of chat 10/20/21, 12pm EDT https://deepfreeze/dfd/]

@notmydayjob: Thanks for showing up, people

@justicewarrior: I almost didn't

@teacherpreacher: I can't say I'm completely at ease with this

@strongcoffee: Whose idea was this, anyway?

@workingmom: Someone who knows who we are

@deepdiver: and probably where we live

@notmydayjob: Let's calm down. A lot of people know who you are by now. Tom Levy and Tasha Wright, the police, maybe other agencies

@truthsleuth: the killer

@dedicateddetective: I bet @notmydayjob knows who we are

@truthsleuth: Does he?

@teacherpreacher: Do you?

@notmydayjob: It's kind of my jam. Don't worry, I haven't shared your identities. But I can help anyone who wants to beef up online security

@justicewarrior: Are you seriously shilling for work?

@deepdiver: or hunting for victims

@notmydayjob: Come on. A clever killer wouldn't be so obvious. Just cuz someone knows your ID doesn't mean they're at your door. The murders were inside the five boroughs, okay? No one on today's call lives inside the city limits, am I right?

@workingmom: Even if you are, some of us who live outside New York still work in it

@justicewarrior: true

@strongcoffee: Again, what's the purpose of this chat?

@deepdiver: We're not all here

@notmydayjob: That's always true with these chats. And this one was scheduled last-minute

@justicewarrior: Why?

@dedicateddetective: Maybe we're supposed to talk about the threat

@deepdiver: *Says* who?

@truthsleuth: Maybe we should hear from brains&beauty, who stirred the pot. What do they have to say?

@deepdiver: I was wondering that myself

@notmydayjob: brains&beauty isn't on today

@truthsleuth: do you know why?

@strongcoffee: Can we get back to why we were called together?

@teacherpreacher: to help the police, right?

@notmydayjob: It was Tom's idea. Well, it was mine first. I reached out to him to offer our help. Told him he had some mental firepower among the DFDs

@dedicateddetective: Gee, thanks

@workingmom: Did you offer to put us in harm's way?

@deepdiver: Yeah, who made you our leader?

@teacherpreacher: Do the police know we're doing this? Are they monitoring us? Is Tom?

@notmydayjob: Tom isn't online. He's wrecked by the thing with Tasha.

@justicewarrior: you mean her torture and death

@dedicateddetective: what?

@strongcoffee: what the ever-loving hell are you talking about?

@workingmom: it just hit the news. Tasha Wright was killed, probably by the Dry Ice Killer.

@teacherpreacher: the hell you say

@countyhunter: How do you know she was tortured?

@justicewarrior: I have friends inside NYPD.

@notmydayjob: Interesting. Are you a cop?

@justicewarrior: (inserts laughing emoji) No

@workingmom: are you a reporter?

@justicewarrior: strike two

@dedicateddetective: I think we can assume the police are monitoring this chat

@deepdiver: Do you think that's why some people aren't on?

@truthsleuth: Have we all decided the killer is one of us?

@workingmom: Doesn't seem fair to point fingers at ppl who aren't here to defend themselves

@notmydayjob: Presence or absence is not the takeaway here

@deepdiver: what is?

@dedicateddetective: our shared identity as Deep Freeze Detectives

@justicewarrior: We're being targeted because someone has it in for Tom or Tasha?

@truthsleuth: or because we already know each other

@notmydayjob: Bingo

@teacherpreacher: Do you know us?

@notmydayjob: Does anyone know anyone?

@workingwoman: Don't be smart. Are we connected through our true crime hobby? Did we meet IRL?

@strongcoffee: Where are you going with this?

@notmydayjob: Has anyone here heard directly from the police?

@teacherpreacher: Why?

@notmydayjob: True confession. The police came to visit me yesterday. Two detectives I won't name. They wanted me to provide a couple of alibis for a couple of the killings. Not hard, since I'm not the killer. They probably wanted to find out what I'd learned while I was researching

@justicewarrior: You mean hacking

@workingmom: What exactly is it you do, @notmydayjob?

@notmydayjob: I have computer skills. It makes sense they'd come and see me

@deepdiver: But do you have dry ice skills

@truthsleuth: might ask you the same question

@notmydayjob: They also asked me questions about my involvement with all things true crime. Like did I belong to any other chats, listen to any other podcasts, visit any other websites, or attend any conferences, hang IRL with other fans?

@workingwoman: I knew it!

@truthsleuth: So have we met in real life?

@teacherpreacher: bet we have

@notmydayjob: I'm not the only one who's been contacted

@strongcoffee: I got a call but not a visit

@deepdiver: ditto

@justicewarrior: I got a message to call

@teacherpreacher: same here

@workingmom: I got a visit. At my place of work, which I did not appreciate

@justicewarrior: Now I want to know what YOU do

@workingmom: Why don't you ask our computer hacker? He seems to know everything

@notmydayjob: not everything

@deepdiver: So we need to figure out who we pissed off on a chat or at a live conference

@countyhunter: Is that our job? Seems dangerous. We could flush out the killer or send them underground. Why not cooperate with the police, let them do the hunting?

@justicewarrior: Can't it help the police if we brainstorm? Do you think it's unsafe to throw out theories or even to chat?

@countyhunter: I can't say. I'm inclined to agree with @notmydayjob that those of you who don't live or work in the area are probably removed from harm's way. On the other hand, the killings are happening closer together, which suggests the killer is getting bolder or more desperate

@deepdiver: You sound like police.

@teacherpreacher: Are you police?

@countyhunter: I'm a fan with a practical streak

@workingmom: So how do we stay safe?

@countyhunter: There are things you can do. Make sure you're never alone. Don't go anywhere by yourself, day or night. Don't meet up with anyone you don't know well, which probably includes your fellow Deep Freeze Detectives. Report anything strange. Talk with the detectives who contact you. Beef up your online security or stay offline. The police are aware of you. Good news for everyone but the killer.

@workingmom: Yeah, you're police

@strongcoffee: @countyhunter, do you expect us to lock ourselves away?

@teacherpreacher: Thought we were done with all that

@truthsleuth: Sounds like we're just getting started

@countyhunter: It may not be much longer

@strongcoffee: from your mouth

@notmydayjob: Solid suggestions from someone who works for the county but as what? A discussion for another chat. For now, keep your head down and your online profile low

@workingmom: Okay, I think we're done here. @notmydayjob, since you're so chummy with Tom, you can let him know we're keeping a low profile as a group.

@teacherpreacher: I think any of us who want to reach out individually should do that.

@notmydayjob: sounds about right

@justicewarrior: hope that's good enough

@deepdiver: it's gonna have to be

[end transcript]

Chapter 28

Sam closed the laptop at Holder's desk back at the Gramercy Park Precinct and rubbed her eyes. She was flagging, but only a little, thanks to five cups of coffee. The captain was down at One Police Plaza, NYPD headquarters for an emergency meeting. The couch in her office looked as if it might be a nice place to lie down. She talked herself out of trying it out.

She considered what, if anything, she'd just learned on the unexpected chat. The remaining DFDs lived outside of the five boroughs but some still worked in the city. How safe were they? Did her presence on the chat offer a measure of security? Could NYPD provide more? Maybe that would have to wait until the new task force met. Or maybe they didn't have that kind of time.

Her phone played. Gordy.

"Just wondered if you need some backup?" he asked. "Or we can build a gym at the office so you can keep up with your weightlifting?"

"What did you hear now?"

"Remember, I used to be a Baltimore detective. My ex-CO has a cousin who works for the forensic division of the Manhattan DA's office. Long story short, plenty of people know about the Dry Ice Killer because of this cousin and because a certain Talbot County lieutenant keeps turning up in the center of things. Did you really deadlift a broken steel door?"

"Yes. Unfortunately, it took two tries. My feet took a hit, although it could have been worse."

"Yikes!"

She grunted. "That's not the half of it. Who else knows?"

"Probably everyone," Gordy said. "By the way, our very own Senator Sean Parker called over to Sheriff Reed. The topic, from what little I can gather, was you."

Sam didn't trust herself to respond.

"Lieutenant? Something wrong?"

"No, no. I just can't believe someone like that would check me out based on one encounter at a cocktail party."

"Sheriff Reed praised you to the sky if that helps to know. He also suggested the senator contact you directly."

"Thank the sheriff for me. No, I'll call him myself. Then I'll give the senator a call."

A couple of seconds of dead air. Then, "Are you thinking of leaving us, Lieutenant?"

"Gordy, I don't know what Senator Parker wants, but I don't have any other plans."

"All right, then. Keep us up to date." Gordy disconnected.

Sam had started to boil during the call, and she was still fuming when it ended. Where the hell did Parker get off, calling Terry, calling her boss, throwing his weight around with the NYPD, which she believed he'd done? If he had a problem with her—or an offer to make her; she didn't really care at this point—let him come to her.

Maybe he was forcing her hand. Fine. She could call right now and demand to speak with Uncle Quinn. Or leave a message with the chief of staff. Something like, "Could you please ask the senator if he attended my brother's wedding back in 1994 to protect my family or to kill us all? Thanks so much." That could earn her at least a FaceTime encounter.

Holder popped back into her office. "How's it going?" she asked.

"I don't even know what I'm looking at anymore," Sam replied. "What's in the bag?"

"Brought you lunch, Lieutenant. You gotta keep up your strength." She placed a wrapped sandwich and a bottle of sweetened iced tea in front of Sam and pulled up a spare chair. "Hope you like it."

"Chicken salad," Sam exclaimed. "Absolutely perfect. Thank you, Jessica."

They ate in companionable silence. Sam forced herself not to bolt her food. Working while injured seemed to burn up a lot of calories.

"I have notes on the two interviews you asked for," Holder said when they'd finished. "Kevin Turner and Regina Young. Detectives Carlisle and Nichols handled both of those. Seems to be a difference of opinion." A grin tugged at the corner of her mouth.

"You have your own opinion?"

"Not me," Holder replied. "I'm the finder. I leave the interpretations to others. Speaking of which, the DFDs are very solid with their alibis. I haven't found anyone who claimed to be at home alone with Netflix, a cat, and a bowl of popcorn."

"Sounds convenient," Sam said. "Then again, New York is not a city of slackers. Let me see what you've got."

"All right. I'm going to make some coffee."

Sam pushed aside her half-eaten sandwich and scanned the reports. Turner was interviewed at his parents' upper East Side townhouse, a piece of real estate Sam imagined to be north of eight figures. Regina Young was at her job at a pediatric dentist's office when they called on her. Neither seemed particularly pleased to be interrupted at work, although for Turner, it was more about time management and less about a boss noticing the presence of two NYPD detectives.

Carlisle's assessment boiled down to Turner's being arrogant but pleasantly so, a smart man being paid well to use his brain. His home setup allowed him to ride out the pandemic while still pleasing his remote and apparently generous employer.

All in all, Turner struck Carlisle as being grievance-free and outgoing, a man unlikely to derive any pleasure from torturing his victims.

Young was indeed related to a victim whose kidnapping was never solved. Yet she seemed almost resigned to inequalities within the justice system and to the challenge of tracking down a beautiful young woman who disappeared. Meanwhile, her son was an honors student, her home a neat and tidy row house she owned free and clear. She seemed to enjoy her job and the company of her young patients. Her boss declared he a national treasure, a conclusion with which her coworkers agreed.

Not killer material, Carlisle concluded.

Nichols took a decidedly non-benevolent view of the subjects. Turner, she declared, was full of himself, a narcissistic misogynist who might well derive great pleasure out of hurting others. He had the computer skills to fake his own alibis and identify and locate his victims.

As for Young, she radiated resentment as far as Nichols was concerned. Her very particular expertise in working in the mouths of young children told Nichols the woman had the ability to inflict damage. The detective also concluded that Young's many friends might be more than willing to provide alibis.

Sam sat back, puzzled. No two detectives ever saw things in exactly the same way. Experience colored first impressions. Still, partners usually ended up on the same page, at least in successful investigative pairings. How did Carlisle and Nichols reach such different conclusions about their persons of interest?

Her phone rang, giving her the impetus to vacate Holder's office for the empty conference room.

"Hey, Danny. How is the mood at the Cold Case headquarters?"

"Dark, which you'd expect, and determined, which you'd also expect. Chloe's here. We're going through Tasha's old cases with help from her former partners. Trying to see if we can match any of them to our DFD profiles."

"How is Chloe?"

"What? She's fine."

"This morning ..."

"Yeah. The shock of seeing Tasha sent her into a temporary tailspin. I think we were all a little shook up."

I don't buy it. The thought popped unbidden into Sam's head. She decided to keep it to herself. For now.

"How was the online chat?" Carlisle asked.

"I'd like to say illuminating, but I didn't learn much, except people are shook up. Oh, and a few regulars were missing. The rest were ready to go all Salem witch trials on the absent ones."

"Hard to defend yourself when you're not present and accounted for."

"Pretty much what Kevin Turner said. By the way, I read the notes you and Nichols submitted after yesterday's interviews. Day and night.

"How do you mean?"

"You don't see them as stone-cold serial killers. Nichols seems ready to crown one or the other as the Dry Ice Killer."

"I haven't read her report ..."

"You were there. I'm not trying to pry. I just want to get an idea as to what happened."

"It's fine. Turner is self-confident. Puffed up but why wouldn't he be? He's smart, rich, not bad-looking, and he knows it. But he's upfront about it. He could be a sociopath, sure, but I didn't sense it. Honestly, I kind of liked the guy. Young is direct to the point of being blunt. Again, a quality I appreciate. And she adores her patients." He paused. "Maybe Nichols doesn't like quite that much honesty."

Sam let that comment go by. "Who's left to see in person?" she asked instead. "Puzzlemaven and seenitall, right?"

"Yes. I'm willing to put the author on the back burner, though Lopez is jonesing to meet him. That leaves the physician assistant who, by the way, called this morning with alibis. One of them was his mother, so I don't know how much stock we can place in that. I'll probably take a run at her just to confirm."

"What about a face to face with her son?"

Carlisle snorted. "PAs seem to be very busy. Kostakis can give us ten minutes."

"When?"

"Zielinski is hung up at the scene. Lopez is at the studio where Levy is hard at work planning a tribute podcast for his former cohost. Ever the professional, I guess. Ron thinks this might be a good time to spring our visit, maybe without an appointment."

"You and Nichols?"

A slight hesitation. "She's staying here. Do you want to join me?"

"Sure. I'll clear my schedule. Holder needs her space back so she can manage the calls coming in from the other DFDs."

"Great. I'll get you in an hour and we'll take FDR straight up. Three p.m., we should be able to avoid traffic in at least one direction."

"What if it isn't him, Danny? Or any of them?"

"Don't even think that way, Tate."

Chapter 29

"Nice location for a hospital," Sam observed as they walked from the parking lot on East 102nd Street. "How does a patient score a room with a view of Central Park?"

"My mother's friend stayed in a private patient suite and it's all Ma can talk about now," Carlisle replied. "'It was like a hotel, Danny,' she said. 'Put me there if I need a hospital.' Like we could afford it."

He stopped walking and consulted his phone. "Kostakis works in the hospital's cardiac care unit. Sounds important."

"Is he expecting us?"

Carlisle shook his head. "Nope. I cleared it with his supervisor, but I figure we'll surprise him, just like we did some of the other Deep Freeze Detectives. We're here. Masks up."

Kostakis kept them cooling their heels in the main lobby for half an hour before directing them to an upper floor in the cardiology wing. They found him leaning against the reception desk, looking at his phone. He was a solid man, strong through the shoulders, a little soft under the chin. The dark blue scrubs hid a slight paunch. Not fat, but not an athlete's body, either. Heavy eyebrows hung over nearly colorless eyes, maybe blue, maybe gray. They rested briefly on his visitors, then fixed on a spot behind them.

Kostakis put his phone on the counter and pulled up his mask. He made no move to approach the visitors.

"Good morning, detectives," he said. He spoke in a pleasant monotone. "I'm Alex Kostakis. Sorry for the delay. I wasn't expecting you." The eyebrows moved down ever so slightly.

"I'm Detective Tate and this is Detective Carlisle," Sam said.

"Pleasure to meet you." He offered a slight nod as his eyes traveled to Sam's sandal-clad foot. "That looks painful. Have you had it checked out?"

"I have, thank you."

His concern evaporated. "Down to the business of why you're here, then. We're all pressed for time. I understand you have some questions about the recent gruesome murders and how they might relate to the true crime podcast I occasionally listen to."

"And the podcast's chat room you seem to frequent," Carlisle said, his voice betraying a slight irritation.

Kostakis moved his gaze to Carlisle's face before sending it back to the far wall. "Some people relax by watching football," he said. "I log in anonymously to discuss cold cases. I hope that's not a crime."

"Not at all," Sam said. "We really do appreciate your cooperation, Mr. Kostakis."

"PA Kostakis," he replied matter-of-factly.

"Excuse me?"

"A physician assistant is a trained and licensed medical professional, Detective Tate. We take the same courses and develop the same skill sets as doctors. Yes, we spend less time in school, no, we don't technically receive a medical degree. The timeline is compressed because we can bypass residency. Nevertheless, we share a knowledge base with the physicians. Just as you might say 'Nurse Jones,' you would say 'PA Kostakis.' To do so acknowledges the abilities of the person who holds the title. It's like calling you Detective Tate." His half-smile seemed like an effort.

"I see. Thank you for clearing that up, PA Kostakis. I had no idea."

"Mind you, some PAs are fine if patients use their first names, especially in an office setting. I'm not in an office setting as you can see." He moved an arm to indicate his surroundings.

"Do you actually perform surgery?" Carlisle asked. "I thought only doctors did that."

"As I said, we're virtually the same thing," Kostakis answered. "Especially when it comes to surgical assistance. These days, with the doctor shortage, a surgical PA will do a lot of the same work physicians did in the past."

"Impressive," Sam said. "A surgical physician assistant sounds almost like a specialist."

"More of a well-qualified generalist, but I take your point." He seemed to relax under her compliment. "Actually, we know a great deal more about the nuts-and-bolts operation of the profession. At the same time, we have a great deal of medical knowledge in common with the most rigorously trained specialists. I've performed a number of routine procedures, of course; I've even assisted in more challenging operations. In truth, I've probably spent more time in an operating room than your average general practitioner, not to mention almost any other PA in this hospital."

"I see." Sam nodded. "What else does your job involve?"

Kostakis twisted his head slightly, making the absence of color in his eyes even more pronounced.

"Intake, including patient history, preliminary exams, writing prescriptions, making recommendations, initiating follow-up, and, as I mentioned, more routine procedures in the operating theater. Assistance at every level. We step out front as needed."

"That's very impressive," Carlisle said. "All that responsibility on top of which you care for your mother, is that right?"

Kostakis narrowed his eyes ever so slightly.

"I'm not certain what my private life has to do with your inquiries, Detective. As for what my job involves, I could offer a more detailed overview but not today." Kostakis glanced at a nearby wall clock. "If you need alibis and that sort of thing, over and above what I already provided, I can get you more information. If you think it's necessary to go over the same ground, that is."

"We're really hoping you might be able to shed some light on the murders in terms of your fellow detectives' reactions to them," Carlisle replied. "You do realize you're the only medical expert among the Deep Freeze Detectives who regularly shows up to chat."

Kostakis inclined his head. "I'm not certain how that makes me an expert on murder. We're in the practice of saving lives here, not taking them. However, if you're soliciting my impressions of the other so-called detectives, I am willing to share those. The one called notmydayjob seems particularly impressed with his abilities."

"His abilities?" Sam asked.

"His wit, his knowledge, his skill set, which I gather from his comments have something to do with computers. And yes, I said 'he,' though I might be mistaken. Women are less inclined to boast. Except for brains&beauty. That individual, whom I judge to be female, has no problem reminding us how clever she is." Kostakis delivered his judgments in an affectless tone.

"Have you met any of these people in real life, PA Kostakis?" Sam asked. His face shuttered. "I suppose it's possible. I attended a conference a year or two ago. But I wouldn't know anyone's name. These chats are anonymous."

"You seem comfortable enough on a computer to penetrate the layers," Carlisle observed.

"My firewall, you mean. Yes, I've taken great care with my own security. I don't have any interest or time in seeing about anyone else."

"Thank you for your insights," Sam said.

Kostakis wasn't finished.

"I do have an affinity for problem-solving the others seem to lack. Again, I don't know how that will help you."

"How do you mean?" Sam asked.

"There is a right way and a wrong way to approach a puzzle," Kostakis explained. "Everyone likes to emphasize thinking outside the box, looking at a problem from as many angles as possible. But at some point, it comes down to two central issues. Details matter. Process matters. One provides clues, the other provides a framework within which those clues can be assessed. It's a concept many people, including most amateur detectives, don't seem to respect. Of course, you do. You're professionals."

That last line was delivered without any inflection, so that Sam couldn't tell if it was meant ironically or not.

"Now, if you'll excuse me, Detectives, I really do need to get back to work," Kostakis said. He remained as he was, a statue with poor posture and restless eyes.

"I think we've been dismissed," Carlisle muttered.

"In more ways than one," Sam replied. She turned to the elevator, certain that the man who hadn't once made direct eye contact during their conversation was now watching them intently.

Chapter 30

Zielinski called early the next morning, just as Sam was finishing her second cup of coffee.

"Feeling better?" he asked.

"Coming along," Sam answered. She glanced at her bare feet. The bruises still looked hideous, a paint smear of mismatched colors, but the swelling was way down. She could almost wiggle her toes. "Good. Keep using your cane, even if you don't think you need it. Listen, Theo Austin wants to see us."

"She's better?"

"She's awake. The good news is she probably won't need throat surgery. The bad news is she can't really talk. I guess she's using some sort of hand signals plus a pad of paper. She's determined to communicate with us. With you, since you saved her life."

"Where's everyone else?"

"Danny's meeting with his CO. Lopez is on her way to the precinct to meet with ours. Chloe will meet us there."

Sam almost swore out loud. She made a fist and punched her leg. "I'm sure she has other investigations to work on," she said.

"I think we need to keep someone from Queens North Homicide in the loop on this."

"Of course. See you there."

She telephoned Dimitri, who promised to be there as soon as possible. The idea that she had a car and driver on call amused Sam. Once again, she marveled at the connections her aunt had made over the course of a lifetime confined to this Queens neighborhood.

On the way into Brooklyn, she telephoned Sean Parker's office and requested an online meeting with the senator to discuss his interest in her. Provocative without being overly aggressive. Not that she could measure its effect based on the carefully worded and utterly innocuous response from the receptionist about delivering the message.

She met Zielinski in the lobby of the medical center hospital around 10 a.m. "Austin's been moved out of the ICU and into a private room," he said. "She's also got a private duty nurse, and the head of gastroenterology is personally handling her case."

"Sounds like progress," Sam said. "Who pulled what strings to get her the extras?"

"No one from NYPD, as far as I know. Or the mayor's office."

"Theo Austin has friends with leverage," Sam said. She looked around. "Where's Nichols?"

"Running late. She can catch up." The cop outside Theo Austin's room was young, masked, and alert. Head was up, not down to his phone. He jumped to attention as they approached.

"She's got a visitor, detectives," he announced. "Dude's been in there since late yesterday afternoon. She's allowed a maximum of two people at a time, so you'll have to work it out. I don't care, but the nurses are sticklers for the rules." He grinned under his paper mask.

Sam found herself smiling back at him.

"Thank you, officer," Zielinski said. "If you need a break ..."

"If it's all the same with you, I'll stay here until my shift ends."

"Very good." Zielinski knocked, waited two beats, and entered with Sam.

Theo was propped up with three or four fluffy pillows that looked nicer than any Sam had seen in a hospital setting, as did the nightgown and the bright blue comforter on the bed. A brownish drink, which might have been a Frappuccino, sweated next to her on the nightstand.

A long-legged man with silver-streaked brown hair and a worried expression sat in a chair he'd pulled as close as possible to the bed. His knees were pressed to the bed frame, and he held one of Theo's much smaller hands in both his own.

Her father? Sam wondered and then corrected herself. This man wasn't old enough to be a generation ahead. Maybe a brother, a colleague, or a special friend.

Austin appeared wan under the less than flattering glare of the hospital lighting. Her freckles almost disappeared against her pale skin. By contrast, the bruises around her jaw were equal to any gained by a prize fighter on the losing end of a glove. Her hair was flat against her head, the color muted, as if coated with rust and sand. A thick gauze bandage encircled her neck; a couple of fingers on her left hand were similarly bandaged.

Fortunately, her enormous cobalt eyes appeared unclouded. She waved as they entered

If Austin was glad to see them, the man was less so. He leapt to his feet, fairly quivering with disapproval at the intrusion.

"May I help you?" he demanded.

“Detective Sergeant Ron Zielinski and Lieutenant Sam Tate. Ms. Austin requested we visit her as soon as possible. We hurried right over.”

Sam covered her surprise at Zielinski’s use of titles. He must have known something she didn’t.

“Oh, right, the detectives. I didn’t think meeting with you so soon after the incident was such a great idea. She’s only just woken up, you know. But she can be quite insistent.” The tall man had a British accent, just a suggestion of posh but toned down perhaps for the Americans. His attitude softened marginally. “Sorry. Don’t mean to come across like a mother hen.” He stuck out his hand. “Gregory Davies. Greg is fine.”

“Nice to meet you,” Zielinski said. “How are you connected to Ms. Austin, if you don’t mind me asking?” He didn’t sound as if he cared if Davies minded.

“I’m a major investor in her company. And a, um, close friend.” He colored ever so slightly.

Business partner and special friend. Sam made a mental note. She knew without looking that Zielinski had done the same.

“Er, hospital regulations don’t allow three people in the room at one time,” Davies said. “Perhaps one of you can step out?”

“How about you and I step out, Mr. Davies? Sam here can communicate with Ms. Austin. Meanwhile, we can chat in the lounge. I’m sure you can help me with a couple of details.”

“Oh?” He looked disconcerted. “But Theo can’t really talk. Just whisper. She writes things down, you see.”

“We’ll be just fine,” Sam told him.

“I’d really like to get some information from you, Mr. Davies,” Zielinski said. “Trust me, the NYPD is grateful for any assistance." He put a hand under the man's elbow and herded him toward the door.

"Well, if you're certain. Theo, dear? Will you be alright? Can you tell the detective if there's anything you need? Anything at all?"

Austin smiled, which immediately took ten years off her face. She gave a gentle wave that managed to convey both affection and dismissal.

When the two men left, she made the sign of a heart with her hands.

"He seems fond of you, too," Sam observed. "An investor and perhaps more than that?"

Austin inclined her head and lifted a shoulder. Sam took the response as an affirmation of sorts. No doubt Zielinski would dig deeper to learn more about the relationship. Love and hate could easily occupy the same space.

The woman in the bed made the sign again and pointed to Sam, then herself.

"If you're thanking me for getting you out of the warehouse, you're more than welcome," Sam said. She pulled out the chair Davies had vacated and sat down at an angle that let her see Austin's writing pad. "Are you able to talk at all?" she asked.

Whisper, Austin printed. A little

"We'll stick with pad and paper then. Before we get started, do you need anything? Are you in any pain?"

Austin shook her head.

"Good. Okay, Theo. Let me start with some observations. Call it housekeeping. Then I will listen to, or read, what it is you want to tell me. Will that work for you?"

Austin nodded and gave a thumbs up.

"First of all, you should be aware that we know your real name is Teresa Albon. Not a lot about you we could find, except you were born and grew up in northern Maine with at least one sibling and two parents. No problems, no record, nothing that seemed to necessitate an identity change. So why the new name?"

New career, new gender-neutral name

"I can see that," Sam said. "What was your interest in becoming a DFD?"

Research

Sam rolled her eyes. "I'll let that go for a minute," she said. "Let's skip to the night at the warehouse. Do you know who attacked you? Did you see his face?"

Austin shook her head and wrote:

He stayed behind me the whole time. I couldn't move.

"I don't know if anyone told you, but I shot someone in the foot. A man, judging by the noise he made. He got away, obviously. I didn't hear him speak, though. Did you?"

Just muttering

"Okay, don't worry about that. It was you who summoned me to a meeting, right? When did you figure me for a police officer?"

Austin jotted down:

@countyhunter is 2 obvious

So much for the back story, Sam thought. "Why did you want to meet me at such an out of the way place?"

To talk abt killer ID

Sam almost sprang out of her chair. "What? You know who it is? The Dry Ice Killer?"

Austin shook her head

Suspicions

"And you wanted to talk to me about them. Who else did you talk with about your suspicions or about having a meeting?"

Tasha Wright. Sat night

A Saturday night meeting, after which Tasha was killed.

"Why didn't you come into the precinct?"

Tasha wanted to do podcast first

"Podcast? Were you planning a podcast about the Dry Ice Killer with Tasha?"

Tues. Good 4 ratings, good for TCCon, good for police. Win-win

Sam's anger startled her; it swept away any sympathy she'd brought with her into the room. Brains&beauty had dropped enough hints on the chat to concern the killer. Maybe that person had identified her and even followed her to the meeting. Sam didn't want to imagine what the killer had done to Wright to extract information from her.

She forced her voice to stay steady. "You were going to speculate on air about the identity of a dangerous killer without proof?"

Austin shook her head and scribbled:

Tasha said she'd get proof. She texted me Mon to set up a meeting w/you & she'd be there

"Tasha is dead, Theo. Tortured and killed with dry ice. Probably early Sunday, although we just found her body this morning. The killer must have used her phone to text you."

Austin's hand went to her mouth. Her eyes filled with tears.

Sam laid a hand on the woman's shoulders. "I'm sorry. It's a lot to take in. No, don't," she ordered as

Austin thumped herself on the chest. "Tasha's death is not your fault. The blame lies with the bastard who is doing this. Got it?"

Austin nodded miserably.

"Theo, as long as your hand can hold up, we'll keep going. I know it's rough. If you need a break, we can take one. Anything that occurs to you, you let me know. However, I don't want you to share it with anyone else for now, not even your friend Greg. Is that clear?"

YES!

"Good. Now write down anything else you can think of. Suspicions, recollections, whatever. Take your time." Sam sat.

After a couple of seconds, Austin held up a finger, then wrote:

I ID'd DFD regulars and checked them against a list of ppl at my first TCCON. Looking for suspects. The women dropped off my list. They were team players, even the dental tech. Couple of men stood out. A little too high and mighty.

"Arrogance is not a crime, Theo," Sam said.

Austin appeared to concede the point. She scribbled:

Several men from TCCon's physical and virtual conferences ended up on the chat. I pegged them right away. Same attitude, same words

"There are a couple of men on the chat who might not be pleasant to know in real life. That doesn't make them killers." She paused. "Wait a minute. You said, 'same words.' What did you mean by that?"

Hard to explain

"Are you thinking about a particular phrase or slogan?"

It's fuzzy

"Understandable. We can pick this up later."

Austin held up a finger, as if to say, "wait." She looked off, then resumed writing.

Killer said something b4 I fainted

Sam felt her gut clutch. "Do you remember what it was?"

Austin whispered a single word that sounded as if it had been dragged over broken glass.

"Respect."

Chapter 31

Austin was through. Sam fluffed her pillows and left with a promise to return. She found Zielinski sitting in the nearby visitors lounge with Gregory Davies. The two men were sharing a laugh, suggesting less an interrogation and more a pleasurable exchange. Unless Davies was a psychopath.

"Detective Nichols is in the ladies' room," Zielinski said. "She'll join us in a minute."

"I think I'll wash my hands," Sam said. Zielinski nodded

She pushed open the door and headed to the double sink. Nichols obviously occupied one of the two stalls, which she exited a moment later, head down and hand in her purse.

She looked up, saw Sam, and yelped. The bag slid off her shoulder, dumping its contents on the floor. The two-word curse she yelled, along with her outsize reaction to Sam's presence seemed so out of character that Sam almost laughed. Until Nichols fell to her knees and, ignoring her wallet and her phone, frantically scrambled after several loose capsules that rolled across the floor.

"Here, let me help you." Sam moved to join her.

"I don't need your help," Nichols snapped. "You've done enough. Nearly gave me a goddamn heart attack as it is. Back off!"

Sam retreated to the sink and watched the detective scoop up the pills and throw them back in her bag, except for one she dry-swallowed. She sat back on her haunches, her body trembling, and drew her breaths in and out much the way Sam did when she was trying to calm herself.

Sam didn't think the yoga technique was what slowed the woman's heart rate and stopped her shaking.

After a minute Nichols closed, then opened her eyes. Only then did she retrieve her other items and put them back into her bag with slow, deliberate movements.

"Chloe, can you stand?" Sam asked.

"Of course I can." She stared at Sam with distaste. Her pupils were tiny dots in a sea of lead. "I'm fine." She got to her feet and dusted off her skirt.

"Chloe, if you have a problem ..."

"You're my problem, Tate. You and a bad back, but that I can handle."

"Is that what the pills are for?"

Nichols walked to the sink. She made a show of washing her hands. She spoke into the mirror.

"Why are you working on this case, Lieutenant? You're not NYPD. You don't even live here. Is it the glory? The challenge? Are you going for a record? Most serial killers caught by one person. Or does my good-looking partner, Detective Danny Carlisle have something to do with your interest?"

"I get it, Chloe. You resent my presence." Sam made no attempt to approach. "You have since the day we met. Did you draw press attention my way, maybe even give the story a negative spin? So you could get some of the rank and file to question my role, maybe force me to stand down?"

"I never—"

"It doesn't matter right now. What matters are the pills in your bag."

"My medicine, you mean. For a very serious injury I sustained in the line of duty." She ever so slightly slurred the word "sustained."

"Chloe, I was sheriff of a Tennessee county with an escalating opioid crisis. Now I work in a county where the problem is even worse. I know the signs of addiction. I know it can affect anyone struggling with pain. Mothers and fathers, young and old, rich and poor, men and women. Doctors, lawyers, cops. Believe me, I'm not judging."

"Like hell you aren't." Nichols stopped rubbing her hands under the running water. She straightened, smoothed back an invisible hair, and faced Sam, defiant.

"I'm sure you'd like to use this issue to get rid of me, Lieutenant. Or humiliate me; I don't know which. It's not going to happen. Things work differently in the big city. Everyone understands what a demanding job this is. I have the trust of my captain and my partner. I have never let my pain define me. My treatment has never interfered with my performance."

Sam thought that might be true. Plenty of people in her line of work used and occasionally abused pills, booze, or who knows what else. Most of them either burned out or let up. Some just kept going.

How long had Nichols been dependent? Was Sam really the first person to notice? Lopez had hinted at an issue. Maybe sympathetic coworkers chose to look the other way. Maybe even Carlisle. While Sam had no illusions about the drug's dangers, she also understood that she was an outsider. Her job, in the short time that remained, was to help stop a killer who was only becoming more active.

"Lieutenant, please." Nichols dropped her defiance like a veil. "I've hit a rough patch. I'll take care of it. I'll see my doctor. I'll get a different prescription. I'll even go back to physical therapy. I want to help catch the guy who killed Tasha. Let me do that."

"Fine. I promise you, though, if you so much as—"

"I get it," Nichols said. "Let's get back to work."

Sam was glad to do that. Unfortunately, her work now included keeping her eye on Detective Chloe Nichols.

Chapter 32

Sam left the ladies' room first. The two men were still chatting. Zielinski stood, which signaled the end of what looked like an amiable exchange. They shook hands like old friends. Davies appeared less anxious, even more so when Sam reported that Austin was fine.

"She is coming along," he enthused. "She's a very strong woman. Detective—Ron—it was very nice to speak with you. Now if you'll excuse me." He strode away on his long legs, back to the room where he'd been holding vigil.

Sam watched him hurry off. "Seems as if you two got along pretty well," she said to Zielinski.

"He's an okay guy. Charming, amusing, slightly self-deprecating, kind of a Hugh Grant type. He's wildly in love with Theo Austin. Not sure if she knows it."

"She knows it," Sam said.

"I don't think he's acting. He's also a big fan of her entrepreneurship. He believes in her company and its prospects over time. Thinks she's brilliant as well as beautiful, blah, blah. Oh, and he's a billionaire several times over. I can't even count that high. Ever heard of TechJet?"

"The company that advertises 'faster than the speed of light' delivery?" Nichols asked. She'd regained her equilibrium, enough so that Zielinski didn't notice anything amiss.

"That's the one. Trains that move so fast you can't see them. Planes that lift off like the old Concord but can be maintained for a fraction of the price. Physical goods that get delivered the same day. 3D backups. It's going to put a number of companies out of business, from DHL and UPS to maybe even Amazon if Davies sets his mind to it."

"Not sure that's necessarily a bad thing," Sam said. "Is he in the business of manufacturing noncommercial aircraft for, say, the military?"

"I wondered the same thing, so I texted Holder to look for connections between TechJet and the company Kevin Turner works for."

Sam looked incredulous. "When did you do all that?"

"Just before Davies and I sat down to talk. I thought I recognized him. Don't look so surprised, you two. I can multitask."

"I would hope so, Detective Sergeant." Sam emphasized the last two words. "I mean, way to drop a career bombshell during an introduction." She slapped him on the back.

"A promotion," Nichols added. "Congratulations. When were you going to tell us?"

"As soon as we caught a break in the case. Did we, Sam? What did Theo have to offer?"

"To start with—"

"Hang on. Lopez is calling." He put his phone on speaker. "You've got me, Nichols, and Tate."

"Hi, there," Lopez said. "Productive day?"

"So far," Zielinski replied. "You?"

"Yep. Captain Platt is all caught up and I've got the information you asked for from Holder."

"Let's have it."

"Davies and Turner work for businesses with different clienteles and probably different mission statements. Turner's company has dealings with DOD and DHS. The only government agency TechJet people have spoken with is FEMA, and that's about delivering emergency supplies. Nothing involving Homeland or Defense. No contracts with any foreign government. They seem more interested in dominating the private delivery service sector."

"Greg Davies may be what he appears to be, a wealthy guy who is smitten with Austin," Zielinski said. "Kevin Turner may be nothing more than a pain in the ass genius."

"I still think he could be our guy," Nichols said.

"He's staying on my list," Lopez declared. "Oh, we got the lab report back on evidence recovered from Tasha Wright's body. Well, we received two reports."

"What do you mean?" Sam asked.

"It's a little puzzling," Lopez admitted. "You met the MLI on scene, right?" "Ginger Baker," Zielinski said. "Female, not to be confused with the famous rock drummer." "Right. That's the report I'm using. But the lab had a partial report from another MLI who arrived earlier. They write everything into a tablet, and everything is saved. This report is marked incomplete. Maybe that's why there's no mention of a red carpet."

"Red carpet?" Zielinski asked.

"Yeah. Baker's findings included samples of red carpet fiber. The lab confirms they came from a cheap polyester long-weave rug just this side of shag. Nothing like the nice stuff they have in Levy's studio, by the way."

"A clue to where Wright was killed," Sam said. "Who signed the other evidence report?"

Lopez took a moment. "That's just it. No signature. Which is weird."

Sam stood stock still, rooted in place by the sensation that several dots were about to connect.

"Hold on, Margarite." Zielinski turned to Sam. "Tate? You okay? What's going on?"

Sam expelled the breath she'd been holding while ideas sorted themselves out. "I'm fine," she said. "Just a lot of thoughts coming together. For starters, I agree with Nichols that we need to have another talk with Kevin Turner."

"I didn't say—"

"Then I'd like to talk with who supervises the MLIs."

"Someone at the OCME's office," Zielinski said.

"Right. How fast do you think we can—?"

She stopped abruptly, aware that she was acting as if she were head of Criminal Command. That was fine back in Talbot County, Maryland. It wasn't remotely appropriate behavior for a temporary consultant to the NYPD.

"I'm sorry, Ron. You're the boss," she added.

"And you're the consultant with the finely tuned instincts. Let me call over to the OCME and see how quickly I can set something up. Margarite, can you contact Kevin Turner and tell him we need to see him this afternoon or tomorrow morning at the latest? Don't make it a choice. Sam, do you have something to add?"

"Let's bring in Kostakis as well. One after another. We can put new people in front of each of them. Me and Lopez on Turner, Chloe and you on Kostakis. Carlisle is our observer. Oh, and Margarite, can you ask Jessica to go back in the chat transcripts a few months and highlight the word 'respect' wherever she sees it?"

"Will do."

"Okay, we all have our marching orders," he said. "Chloe, do you have anything you want to add?"

Nichols was already headed for the elevator bank. "Nope, I'm good," she called out without turning around. "See you tomorrow."

Sam didn't take her eyes off the woman until she rounded the corner and disappeared.

Chapter 33

Sam headed back to Queens on high alert. She could barely sit still on the subway and ended up pacing a near-empty car. No one followed her, at least not that she detected. Her jitters related to her efforts to gather disparate facts, arbitrary impressions, snatched bits of dialogue, and random observations and pull them into a coherent narrative.

She'd long ago decided that the most exhilarating, most stomach-churning part of her job had nothing to do with facing danger. Those feelings piled on as you neared the finish line, just before you dropped in the last piece of the puzzle that had been in your pocket the whole time and stood back to take in the big picture.

Tomorrow she would go through all the pockets to retrieve those missing puzzle pieces. In the meantime, she needed to keep busy.

Danny called just as she got to Rosa's. She brought him up to date, then begged off seeing him in the evening in favor of dinner with her aunt. She reached Terry but he was between meetings and too rushed to talk.

She couldn't run, so she contented herself with as much in the way of calisthenics as she could manage. Not much, thanks to a couple of knots in her neck. A massage would have been nice, but she didn't want to leave the house. She decided on a soaking bath with Epsom salts.

Forty minutes later, she padded downstairs in a fluffy robe Rosa had left for her and checked the refrigerator for something to tide her over.

The phone played her latest ringtone selection, "Stayin' Alive," just as she sat down to eat. She'd downloaded it for its New York–style swagger. Now the chorus had taken on additional relevance. So did the number displayed on the screen. Senator Parker's office.

"Good afternoon, Lieutenant Tate," the polite young woman said. "I hope we're not catching you at a bad time?"

"I've just finished a meeting," Sam replied. She could only hope she was out of range of any video cameras or drones that might give lie to her statement.

"The senator is eager to speak with you. Zoom is fine. He does have time constraints ..."

"Naturally," Sam said as she headed upstairs. "Can we begin in five minutes?"

"I'll send a link," the woman said and hung up. Sam needed two minutes to pull on a sweater, pull back her wet hair and swipe on some lip gloss. She used the remaining three to set up her laptop back downstairs in front of Rosa's tiny bookcase. The lighting was less than optimal, but the background gave the illusion of a professional setting.

She logged on and waited an extra four minutes. Then he was in front of her, filling her screen and looking much as he had a year and a half earlier when Sam and he were introduced. Perhaps a little more silver at the temples. Impeccably tailored in a dark-blue suit with a purple herringbone tie. Now, as then, he wore lightly tinted glasses that partially shielded his eyes. Sam knew them to be similar in shape, size, and color to her own.

"Sam, how nice to see you again," he began in his rolling baritone. "You look well." He leaned in and smiled. She forced herself not to sit back.

"I'm so sorry we aren't meeting in person, although I hope we can make that happen soon. I understand how busy you are, especially since your participation in tracking down that serial killer. I trust you all are making progress."

"We are," she said shortly. "Senator, I'm aware that you called both my former colleague and my current supervisor to talk about me."

"Yes. Each of them wisely suggested I contact you directly, but you've beaten me to it." The smile was warm, sincere, made for the camera and for videoconferencing.

"Both Special Agent Sloan and Sheriff Tanner indicated you wanted to present me with an opportunity."

"That's correct. A career path with more opportunities than the one you're on at this moment. Now, I understand you have a full-time job under the command of an admiring sheriff. Although after your impressive performance in New York, you must be juggling quite a few offers."

"Probably not as many as you think," Sam admitted. "I'm a little, ah, mature to start from the bottom, which is what most city police forces would require. Maybe I'll hear from a county department down the road, although coming in as an outsider doesn't appeal to me anymore."

"What about working in Washington? I don't presume to know exactly how close you and Agent Sloan are, but he is a man with a bright future."

"I don't think the FBI is in the cards for me."

"I'm talking about the Secret Service."

She gaped at the screen. "You're suggesting I apply for a job with the Secret Service?"

"Yes, as a special agent. As you may know, I sit on the Committee for Homeland Security and Governmental Affairs. We oversee DHS and they oversee the Secret Service."

"My age—"

"Won't be a factor for several years due to your status as a veteran. Your police and military experience will likely exempt you from basic training in Georgia, although you'll have to undergo specialized instruction here in DC. I think we can arrange to get you in as a GS-11 or even higher."

She wanted to get up and walk away, maybe even leave the room. But these onscreen encounters were unforgiving that way. She wasn't even sure where to shift her focus.

"Why me specifically?" she managed to ask.

"That's not complicated at all. The agency has encountered more than a few bumps in the road in recent years. Some bad behavior but also some external incidents beyond its control. Morale is a bit low, and several senior agents are retiring. Your experience, your professional profile, even your gender, if we're being candid, would be a tremendous asset."

To the agency or to you? Sam wondered.

"Well," she said at last, "you seem to have worked it all out. I hope you don't mind my asking: Did you also engineer my appointment to the NYPD task force?"

"You've already made progress on the case, as I understand it."

"You didn't answer my question. Sir."

Parker smiled. "The mayor is a friend of mine. I may have offered an opinion on your worth."

"And what is my worth to you, Senator Parker? Or should I say, Uncle Quinn."

If she expected him to look surprised, or even pretend to, she was disappointed.

"So, you know," he said.

"I do now." She had the pleasure of seeing him flinch. "I've been entertaining the possibility since I met you at the gallery opening in St. Michaels. I assume you knew I'd be there, since you made a point of removing your glasses to flash your green eyes at me."

He touched his eyewear. "For your information, the glasses correct vision and mitigate a light sensitivity. And no, I didn't know you'd be there. But I knew you existed. My adoptive parents told me as much."

"Were these the people who worked for the Patriarca family?"

His face clouded. "These were good people who desperately wanted a child and took wonderful care of the one gifted to them."

"Interesting way of putting it," Sam shot back. "I'm curious. Did you ever try to meet your birth parents? My great-uncle and my grandmother? Or your half sisters? You had three." She waited a beat. "You don't need to answer. I know you sought out Colleen. But why did you try to track me down all these years later?"

"I didn't."

His answer brought her up short.

"Then how did you know we were related?"

Parker lifted his glasses. His eyes were hers in masculine form. Without thinking, she reached up and touched her face.

"We met twice, at the same gallery in St. Michaels. We didn't speak the first time, but I was bowled over by your resemblance to your mother and yes, to me. After that, I did make some inquiries, so that I had my own ideas about our connection when we met again."

Was he telling the truth? She floundered and decided to take another tack.

"Do you have siblings or a family of your own?" She already knew the answer.

"No," he said after a few seconds. "Only child. And my wife died in an accident not long after we were married."

"An accident?"

"That's correct."

Sometimes we hurt the ones we love, Sam thought. She wanted to say it out loud, throw it out there along with the accusations and recriminations that festered inside her.

She stared at the screen, saw that the discussion was being taped, considered her options.

"Sam?"

"I was just trying to recall if you were at my brother's wedding in New York back in 1994."

"I wasn't invited," he said simply.

The door opened behind him to reveal a young man in a suit. "Excuse me, sir, but you have that three o'clock."

Parker replaced his glasses and smiled. "Sam, please think about the offer we discussed. I think it would be good for you in so many ways."

He left the chat. Sam stayed where she was, her eyes on the inactive screen, her head and heart in turmoil.

Chapter 34

Sam sat in the passenger seat massaging her temples while Zielinski drove them to the OCME's office for a 9:00 a.m. meeting with the MLI supervisor.

"You need ibuprofen or something?" Zielinski asked.

She was tempted to spill the entire story of Senator Half Uncle to Ron. Except she didn't have enough distance. Despite hashing out her misgivings about Parker with Terry last night, she still woke up to a throbbing headache. The only thing to do was to force her concerns onto the back burner.

One homicide at a time, she reminded herself as they arrived at the facility.

They were greeted by Ezra Pollack, tall and fit, with salt and pepper hair, twinkling eyes, and a mustache that would make a walrus proud. He ushered Sam and Zielinski into his office and closed the door.

"Thanks for taking the time to see us so quickly, Director Pollack," Zielinski said.

"Please call me Ezra. Have a seat and ignore the mess." He gestured to a relatively tidy desk and pulled over a couple of chairs.

"Let me jump right in with the bad news," he began without preamble. "I did some checking after you called yesterday. We have no history of an Alan King working here as an MLI or in any other capacity. Not now, not ever. I even tried alternate spellings on the first name. Nothing."

"I was afraid of that," Sam said.

"However," Pollack continued, "I went a little further. I pride myself on my detecting skills." His grin pushed up a generous mustache up to reveal small, even teeth. "People who use aliases tend to stick with their initials. You'd think after thousands of films, TV shows, and novels ... well, never mind. The point is, I found something."

"An MLI with the same initials," Zielinski prompted.

"Not quite. An applicant. We've had multiple submissions for an MLI position from someone named Alexander Kostakis of Forest Hills, Queens. And by multiple, I mean four."

Sam and Zielinski looked at each other.

"How did Mr. Kostakis apply four times and not get accepted?" Sam asked.

Pollack leaned on his desk and steepled his hands.

"Let me start with what he did get right. He went to CUNY, majored in chemistry, then went on to get an MS as a physician assistant. We require that of all our MLIs. It's one of the reasons the OCME in this city is a national leader in the field of forensic investigation. Kostakis then did a clinical rotation at Mount Sinai. He was twenty-six at the time of his first application."

"Sounds as if he'd put in the work," Sam said.

"Getting through the program is no mean feat. It's like an abbreviated form of med school and it's hard work. But once you're finished, you're finished. No residency or associate positions. You graduate, pass the board exams, and become a licensed PA. Nowadays, it's a smart career choice. PAs are in demand, and the salary is impressive. A lot better than here." He grimaced.

"But Kostakis didn't want to keep working as a physician assistant," Sam noted.

"Apparently not. That could be said of all our applicants, although most spend more time trying it out before applying here. Not that Kostakis failed at his clinical rotation. According to his supervisor, he was quite thorough and excellent with details. He was invited to stay."

"They liked him?" Sam asked.

"Let's just say his supervisors admired his work. He was knowledgeable and thorough. Valuable skills to have in any setting, especially prized in a hospital setting."

"I sense there's more," Zielinski said.

"According to his mentoring physician, he lacked interpersonal skills."

Sam thought about her encounter with Kostakis. "Could he have been autistic?" she asked.

"Possible, I suppose. Unfortunately, autism is all too often used as a catch-all to explain away a range of psychosocial disorders. His supervisor mentioned that Kostakis didn't seem concerned with what other people felt. He was dismissive of colleagues. He didn't connect with his patients. He showed little interest in the human side of the practice."

"A lack of empathy," Sam observed. "Not a great quality in a physician assistant."

"Or a medicolegal investigator." Pollack stretched his long arms and gracefully brought them back to the desk, like a heron settling on the water. Then he continued.

"People assume that since we're working with the dead, feelings like empathy and compassion don't come into play. Plenty of others see what we do as ghoulish. Nothing could be further from the truth. Yes, our people must be able to compartmentalize. You can't approach a dead body in anything but a detached manner or you'll go crazy. But our investigators are kind and caring. They want to honor the dead and help the living. They know that if they do their job effectively, homicide investigations can be moved along, families can be comforted, and sometimes justice can even be served."

He threw up his hands in exasperation. "My wife tells me I step up on the soapbox too much of the time. Apologies."

"Not an issue," Sam said. "Your description fits with a lot of what we do."

"Did you interview Kostakis yourself?" Zielinski asked.

"Not the first time. That was done by a senior MLI. She later admitted she didn't like him. Nothing he said per se, just a bad feeling she had. I was concerned she'd been influenced by the caveats included in his recommendation. Still, first impressions count for a lot around here. We have nearly a thousand applications for just a few openings every year."

Kostakis first applied ten years earlier, the supervisor went on. He wrote a follow-up note even after his application was denied thanking everyone for the opportunity. Two years later, he applied again.

"I handled that interview," Pollack said. "Kostakis still worked at Mount Sinai during the day. He'd also picked up hours at a clinic on the Bowery. Lousy pay, late nights. He performed admirable work, according to everyone there."

"He'd gone from self-centered to altruistic?" Zielinski asked.

"Seemed so, at least on the surface. Then I spoke to him."

They waited while the supervisor considered his words.

"During the interview, we got on the topic of medical ethics when dealing with the deceased. He asked if I thought a dead body could apprehend pain. I thought he was joking. 'Surely your training has taught you the answer is no,' I said, or some such thing. He assured me it did. Yet he couldn't help but wonder, or so he said, whether, if the pain was unimaginable at the end of life, the dead might retain a memory of it."

"Scientific curiosity?" Sam asked.

"Perhaps, but the line of inquiry bothered me. He obviously read my discomfort. He attempted to walk back his remarks. He just dug himself in deeper. He knew it, and he knew I knew it. Just as we both recognized that he'd tanked his chances."

"What did you tell him?"

"I suggested his interests might align better with private sector laboratory work. He acknowledged the recommendation; I can't say that he appreciated it."

"You said he applied again?" Zielinski asked.

Pollack nodded. "Twice more after that, in 2016 and 2018. He was categorically rejected both times. That was the last I heard of him. A year later 'Alan King' made an appearance."

He turned his computer screen around to face the detectives.

"These are the report forms an MLI must file after he or she has completed a preliminary investigation," he said. "We investigate approximately eighty-five hundred deaths per year, more than a hundred and fifty per week. The investigations are handled by forty or so trained MLIs. I don't review those reports. That task falls to the Senior Medical Examiner in each of the five borough offices."

He brought up two files side by side. "These two reports were submitted in Staten Island and Brooklyn, respectively. The first in 2019 and the second in 2020. Both reports were by the book and a hundred percent accurate. Preliminary cause and manner of death were confirmed by autopsy."

"These aren't homicides?" Sam asked.

"No. The first victim was a homeless man who froze to death during a particularly brutal week in December. He was found near a subway stop, poor guy. The second was a woman who was found asphyxiated in a Brooklyn warehouse where she was employed as a catalog specialist. Both classified as accidental deaths by the MLI."

Pollack brought up a third form.

"This form was filed a little less than two weeks ago in Manhattan. A bartender named Grant Paulson was found dead at his place of employment, the Salty Peanut. Noted as a probable homicide." He looked directly at Zielinski. "This was your case, I believe.

"It was."

"Look at the MLI's signature on all three of the forms."

Zielinski bent over the desk. "A. King," he read. "Alan King. The person who identified himself as a medicolegal investigator at several of our crime scenes, although no such person ever worked for the Chief Medical Examiner's Office."

"Correct." Pollack brought up two more files. "And here are the final two reports. Both recent cases, I believe. Both signed by the same person. These came to my attention because the Senior Medical Examiner in Queens couldn't remember anyone by that name. And because the investigations came so close together, just two days apart."

"He'd started to escalate at that point," Sam said.

"Did either of you meet this Alan King at a crime scene?" Pollack asked. "Does he resemble Alex Kostakis?"

"He might," Zielinski admitted. "Or not. He wore a mask, glasses, and a beard which may or may not be real." He shook his head. "I'm not sure we can definitively say one way or the other."

"What kind of person impersonates a death investigator?" Pollack demanded. "A necromaniac?"

A killer, Sam thought.

Chapter 35

"I'd like to get a warrant to search his mother's house," Zielinski said as they made their way uptown."

"That would be ideal," Sam said. "And maybe whatever cubicle or locker he has at the hospital."

"I'd like to get a warrant, Sam, but I don't know if I can. The question is whether we have probable cause."

"Isn't it a crime to impersonate an investigator with the ME's office?"

Zielinski nodded, his eyes on the road. "It is," he said. "But what proof do we have that Kostakis is the same person as Alan King?"

"The Brooklyn detective, Bentley, saw someone identifying as an MLI limp away from the scene after he attempted to process it," Sam said. "We know I shot someone in the foot on Monday night. Most likely male."

"People limp for lots of reasons. Did Kostakis have a problem with his foot that you noticed?"

Sam thought about the interview. "I'm not sure. He didn't move. Stood like a statue. Which is peculiar but not ..." She bit her lip.

"Not evidence. Let's see what Turner has to offer before we decide how to proceed. I don't want to deal with any more people with burned throats or ruptured stomachs or any other signs of torture, believe me. On the other hand, I have to watch my step on this case. I can't let it blow up in my face. Let me ask you this: Can you say with certainty that the fake MLI and the real PA are the same person?"

"King had a full beard, Kostakis had his head covered with a surgical cap. But the eyes ... I could swear they were similar."

"Swear as in a court of law?"

Sam crossed her arms across her chest. "No," she conceded.

"Then we need more."

At the precinct, they ran into Captain Platt, or maybe she'd been waiting for them. "Detective Sergeant," she said in a low voice, "in my office." She turned around to find Jessica Holder just behind her with a pot of coffee. Holder jumped back, and Zielinski followed his CO.

"Detective Sergeant?" Holder asked Sam as they entered the conference room. "When did he get promoted?"

"Recently, I think. Is everyone here?"

"Not yet. Turner's due any minute."

Zielinski returned in five minutes and made a beeline for the coffee. "Where's the team?"

"I'm here," Lopez announced. "Are we ready to get the party started?"

"Ron just finished meeting with Captain Platt," Sam said.

"Uh-oh. Hope we're not in trouble."

"No, Margarite. I do have to update her after we interview Turner. Oh, and she, uh, wanted to know when she could announce my promotion." He flushed. "I asked her to hold off a few days."

"Well, congratulations," Lopez exclaimed. "You deserve it."

"Thanks. Ah, here's Nichols."

Chloe Nichols looked exhausted, even gray under the fluorescent lighting, which only emphasized the dark circles under her eyes. Her pupils were normal, Sam noted, and she was her usual pulled-together self in a neat black pants suit with a blue blouse that unfortunately emphasized her pallor.

Zielinski punched in a number by heart and put the phone on speaker. "Hey, Danny, how far out are you?"

"Don't take my head off, Ron, but I went up to the hospital." Carlisle sounded energized. "I've been gathering information and insights."

"Damn it, Carlisle," Zielinski huffed. "Fine, what did you learn?"

"You first."

"Turns out Kostakis applied to be an MLI with the ME's office four times. We think he decided after the last rejection to impersonate an investigator using the name Alan King. We can't prove it yet."

"How long has this Alan King been working?" Carlisle asked.

"The ME's office uncovered two earlier deaths investigated by someone with that name," Sam said. "Both were ruled accidental. It's possible, given the circumstances, that they were homicides on the order of experiments that were covered up."

"Alan King, the MLI we met at two of our scenes?"

"That's the one," Zielinski confirmed.

"He might have been the bearded guy with glasses who Detective Bentley saw limping away just before we arrived," Sam chimed in. "It's a lot of compelling but circumstantial evidence. Kostakis is clean-shaven. He might have disguised himself, but we didn't notice him limp."

"He has definitely been limping around the hospital," Carlisle rejoined. "According to several of his colleagues, including his supervising doctor, Kostakis claims he has a trick back he's been dealing with for years. It doesn't keep him from doing his job but I gotta ask, does someone like that have the strength to murder several people and maybe, in Tasha Wright's case, move her body?"

Sam's excitement deflated like a party balloon. "He could be faking weakness as part of a long-term strategy. His alibis check out, don't they?"

"I still have to follow through with the mother," Carlisle replied. "I'm sorry, Sam. Wish I had something more definitive."

"It's fine, Danny."

"Wait, when was his first MLI application?"

"Ten years ago," Zielinski replied.

"Interesting," Carlisle replied. "One of the long-time nurses told me that maybe six months after starting at Mount Sinai, Kostakis began applying to medical schools. He believed he could enter as a third year with recommendations from established heart surgeons like his mentor, Dr. Silver. The nurse told me he pestered several doctors for more than a year. They put him off. His moves didn't generate a lot of goodwill among the residents."

"Why didn't the hospital fire him?" Sam asked.

"Short answer, the guy is brilliant. PAs with his abilities in the surgical arena are not exactly a dime a dozen. Silver and the others figured they were getting more than their money's worth as long as he didn't lose them clients. Kostakis seemed to know just how far he could push it. As I said, he's not popular, but he is relatively well-respected."

Sam sat up straight. "How fast can you get back, Danny? We've got Kevin Turner coming in and it would help if you were here."

"I'll see what I can do."

One of the beat cops stuck his head into the conference room to announce Kevin Turner's arrival.

Sam had been expecting an affable-looking guy in a T-shirt, jeans, and overpriced athletic shoes. Maybe a man bun or one of those hipster hats, along with a small goatee. Either on the scrawny side or hefty. Definitely pasty from so many hours spent inside.

The young man who entered could have modeled for GQ. High cheekbones, a straight nose, and strong chin covered by a neatly trimmed beard made up a face that looked like it had been carved out of marble. His light gray eyes were framed by enviably long lashes. The indigo suit and monogrammed pale-blue shirt radiated casual elegance, as did the loafers without socks and the leather pack he wore slung over one shoulder.

Turner wore his wardrobe in a way that intimated monied ease and filled his clothes in a way that suggested regular gym visits and a personal trainer for good measure. No two ways about it: the man was gorgeous. Ten years too young for her and not Lopez's type, but Sam guessed Holder's heart rate had increased.

Nichols didn't look up at Turner's arrival. Maybe his good looks were an irritant.

"Thanks for coming in, Mr. Turner," Lopez began. "I'm Margarite Lopez. This is Detective Sergeant Ron

Zielinski. Officer Jessica Holder is our technical specialist."

"The NYPD version of me," Turner replied. Holder's face colored.

"You've met Detective Nichols," Lopez continued. "And this is Sam Tate, who is serving as a consultant on the case."

The younger man smiled. "Sam Tate, the county sheriff and hunter of serial killers." His emphasis on the words "county" and "hunter" told Sam he'd made the association. That gave her an opening.

"Mr. Turner," she began, "let me get right to the point. You are enough of an expert with digital information that you would have no problem identifying the people on the chat. Let's assume you've already done so. Why?"

His smile widened. "I didn't bother, Lieutenant, not at first. Sure, I was curious about which DFDs I might know from the conference circuit, but I decided it would be more fun to figure out who was who by paying attention to the clues they gave."

"And then?"

"After Theo, a.k.a. Teresa, a.k.a. brains&beauty, put it out there that we might all be targets, I decided to do some more high-level sleuthing. Even though NYPD was already on the case." He turned his handsome face to Holder, who blushed anew.

"Who have you met besides Theo Austin?"

"Regina, Jeff, Esther, Ellen, Grant, Alex, and a couple of others."

"Tell me about Alex Kostakis."

Turner rolled his eyes. "That guy," he said. "I met him at CrimeCon maybe three years ago. He's smart, I'll give you that. He decided we could be best friends, whatever he thought that meant. Maybe he wanted to hang with the other smart kids. I tried to be nice, but the man is a social misfit. Hard to believe he's in the medical profession. He didn't try to fit in; he just expected to be let in."

"What do you mean by that?" Zielinski asked.

"Well, the women outnumber the guys by a huge margin at these conferences," Turner explained. "We could have had some fun. And there are some really nice people there. I've made a lot of friends. I mean, shared interests and all that."

"I gather Alex didn't care about that?" Sam prompted.

Turner shook his head. "Not romance, not friendship, not even a good time. He wanted attention and respect. As if this were a career instead of a silly hobby and he was the guy to teach the rest of us how to solve a crime. Tasha Wright almost laughed him off the video chat last year."

"Did he talk about respect?" Sam asked.

"Hell, yeah. He was like a broken record on the subject."

"Did he get angry when Detective Wright came after him?" Lopez asked.

Turner shrugged. "With Kostakis, it's hard to tell. Being a prick is his default position, if you know what I mean."

"How was he on the chat?" Sam asked.

"Pretty much the same. Annoying, but not seriously so."

"Did he know enough to work out the identities of the other users?"

"He might have, yeah. I showed him how to do that, and as I said, he was intelligent. Before I forget, which of you is impersonating renaissancewoman?"

"What do you mean?" Holder asked. "Renaissancewoman is Ellen Keeley."

"It actually isn't. At least it wasn't during the last two chats." Turner came around the table to stand behind Holder and her open laptop. "The IP address has been spoofed. Check it out." He pointed to her screen. Holder followed his finger and typed onto the keyboard. Turner added a few keystrokes. "See?" he said. "I figured this was your work. I mean, NYPD."

"How did you arrive at that conclusion, Mr. Turner?" Sam asked. She was watching Nichols, who seemed to be watching the door as if someone might burst through it.

"Low-tech plus high-tech. Ellen sent me a postcard last week. Said she was writing friends to let them know she'd be offline for ten days. A yoga retreat in Vermont. No internet, no cell service. I realized it wasn't her on the chat and poked around to see who it was. The road led back to you, or rather, to NYPD."

"Can you narrow down that location?" Lopez asked. "Hold on, Chloe," she said as Nichols began to rise. "Don't you want to know what's going on?"

"I really should check on my partner," Nichols began.

"We'll call him back in a minute," Zielinski told her.

Holder looked up from her keyboard. "The address leads back to Queens North," she reported.

"Sit down, Chloe," Sam said.

Chapter 36

"Officer Holder, Mr. Turner, would you two mind waiting outside?" Zielinski asked.

Neither Turner nor Holder seemed to view the request as a hardship. "Should I continue my research?" she asked.

"Yes," Zielinski replied.

As soon as the door closed, he turned his attention to the woman across the table, her body rigid. "Detective Nichols," he said, "I'm hoping you can help us get to the bottom of this situation. Should I get Detective Carlisle back on the phone so we can decide on the best way to proceed?"

"No, that's not necessary after all. I can help you. I also want to make sure you're not making any assumptions."

"No one's accusing you of anything, Chloe."

"Why do you think we would, Detective Nichols?" Lopez asked.

Nichols glared at Sam. "I have no idea what Lieutenant Tate may have told you or my partner, with whom, by the way, she is very close, about our conversation yesterday, but that was personal and unrelated to whatever you may think is going on."

Sam said nothing, although she took in the sidelong glance Lopez tossed at her.

"I don't *think* anything, Chloe," Zielinski continued. "Lieutenant Tate hasn't said anything to me about whatever transpired between the two of you. In this moment, I'm asking your help in getting to the bottom of a disturbing turn of events. Are we clear?"

She nodded.

"Is there someone within your department who may have a reason for posing as a chat room member without telling the rest of us?"

His words marginally reduced the tension.

"It's something I need to think about," Nichols said. "It would help if Detective Carlisle were here. Do you know when he's expected?"

Sam had her phone on vibrate. She looked down to see a message from Holder.

U need 2 see these

Holder had attached two documents. Sam scanned the first and nodded. This was information she already had. She did the same to the second and barely swallowed the gasp that rose in her throat. Her mind hopped into overdrive, making connections even as she kept her eyes on the tiny screen.

"Sam, is there something you'd like to share?" Zielinski asked.

"Sorry, everyone. I received some information that might help us understand what's going on. It concerns Detective Nichols's oxycodone dependence following a work-related injury five years ago."

Nichols rose from her seat. "You promised!"

"I would never betray your confidence under normal circumstances, Chloe. These are not normal circumstances, however. Please sit."

"It's not like I'm an addict," Nichols snapped. "Whatever problems I had immediately after my injury, and many of my colleagues know that I struggled with pain, I've pretty much resolved them. My judgement is not impaired in the least."

"Hold on." Zielinski raised his hand. "Sam, our job is to catch a killer. I'm not suggesting your observations are meritless. However, if you're suggesting that Detective Nichols can no longer function effectively as a member of this team, you'll have to shoulder the burden of proof."

"I understand. Chloe, who do you list as your emergency contact at work?"

The abrupt change of subject caught not only Nichols but everyone else off guard.

"Let me help you," Sam continued. "Your sister passed away while you were still in the academy. Your parents live abroad. So, who do you list as a local contact? Family? Friend?"

"I don't remember. I probably don't list one."

"The form requires a name. You listed someone at one point. If you later went back and tried to delete that name without putting in a new one, the system defaults to your original choice." She shrugged. "Which means your file lists your aunt."

"Sam—"

"Helena Kostakis of Forest Hills Gardens. Mother of Alex, your cousin, who happens to be a physician assistant. I imagine he has access to various drugs."

Nichols put her head in her hands.

"Is your cousin the killer?" Lopez demanded. "Were you warning him? Keeping him up to date on our progress? Trying to steer us away from him?"

"I don't know! I mean, why would you think that? He's my cousin! We weren't close growing up; he's ten years older than I am. But he's a successful PA, and he takes wonderful care of his mother."

"When did you approach him about getting the oxycodone?" Sam asked. "Or did he come to you?"

"I initiated the contact. This was maybe nine months ago. I had the gold shield; I was transferring to Queens. I'd already exhausted my resources at my old precinct. With everything going on, I couldn't afford to ... to be weak."

She sighed. "Alex was incredibly understanding, especially since his mother suffered from chronic pain. He offered a limited supply of pills as a short-term solution. He really wanted me to get help. I didn't want him to get in trouble. It seemed like the perfect solution, just until I got settled into my new position and got myself a new doctor."

"How did he get the pills to you?" Zielinski asked. It was the first time he'd spoken since Nichols began her story.

"We'd meet once a month in Central Park and he'd give me just enough medicine to get me through. He promised he'd work up a plan that would allow me to taper off. He never asked me for anything, at least not directly."

When they met two weeks ago, Alex was upbeat, Nichols told them. Said he'd had a good week. He wanted to talk about the bartender's murder. She confessed she hadn't heard much beyond the usual chatter as she was now working out of Queens. He pushed just a little, asked if she'd keep him up to date on any new developments so he could share them with other true crime friends of his.

"You didn't think that was strange?" Lopez asked.

"Not really. I wouldn't have pegged Alex as a murder junky, though he's always been drawn to the macabre.

What was strange was that the next case showed up in my jurisdiction."

"The priest's murder at St. Joseph's," Sam prompted.

"Are we supposed to believe you didn't recognize your cousin masquerading as an MLI at the scene?" Lopez asked, her voice rising.

"I never met the investigator at the church. And I never got a chance to speak with whichever investigator showed up at the library." Another glare in Sam's direction.

After that murder, Nichols continued, Alex called her even though they weren't scheduled to meet. He asked her if she'd be willing to participate in a psychological experiment he was conducting. He wanted her to pose as someone named renaissancewoman on his true crime chat.

"And do what?" Sam asked.

"I wasn't sure. He said something about profiling the others. I tried to tell him that was out of my area of expertise. He laughed; told me I had enough training to come up with snapshots."

Nichols was dumbfounded to learn that Sam was going undercover on the chat. "I thought she'd be off the case after, well, after the press debacle," she admitted.

"The one you engineered?" Lopez asked.

Nichols ignored her. "I told Alex. I assumed he wouldn't want two police officers on the chat, but he loved the idea. 'Whatever she suggests, do the opposite,' he told me. I tried, only Sam didn't contribute much. And when she did, I agreed with her. The real surprise was Alex. He immediately latched onto the idea that the detectives were being targeted. I thought he'd be more skeptical."

Alex contacted Nichols after the chat to thank her for participating. He said he'd have the name of a doctor in Queens. In the meantime, he asked if she would give him a peek into the investigation. Nothing classified, he insisted.

"He wanted my impressions of the people on the chat and the people I worked with for a study he was conducting. Especially Sam Tate." Her tone was smug, almost triumphant.

"You were giving him your impressions," Zielinski said.

"Right," Nichols said with relief.

"About us and about our potential suspects," Zielinski continued. "Impressions which would be key components of our criminal investigation and thus confidential."

"And you followed me to Queens last Friday, didn't you?" Sam demanded. "Why? So that I'd be worried the killer was targeting my aunt? So that I'd drop off the case?"

"She did what?" Lopez's body language suggested she was more than happy to throttle the younger detective.

"Everyone, stop." Zielinski put his hands up like a traffic cop. "Chloe, when did you realize your cousin might be the Dry Ice Killer?"

Nichols scanned the room as if she might find an escape route or a place to hide or. She swallowed several times before she managed to choke out a response.

"When the MLI mentioned red carpet fibers, something clicked. I mean, red carpets aren't rare, but

Alex has a kind of a shag rug in his basement laboratory. Hideous thing. I panicked, tried to reach him at work and on his cell. I left messages everywhere. He still hasn't gotten back to me. I don't know where he is."

Sam's phone alerted her to another text. "I need to duck out," she said. "Excuse me a minute."

Zielinski also rose. "We have to get Carlisle in here now." He tried the number. "Damn, it went straight to voicemail."

"He could be stuck in traffic," Lopez suggested.

"Detective Nichols," Zielinski said to the woman slumped in her chair, "you're in trouble. How much trouble is up to Internal Affairs and the Queens DA. I'm going to recommend that you be held for impeding a homicide investigation at the very least. Ideally, Detective Carlisle would escort you back to your precinct. Since he's unavailable, I'll request that your captain send someone over to escort you back. Please stand up. Now, empty your pockets and your bag and place the contents on the table, along with your badge and your weapon."

She did so without protest.

Zielinski picked up the items. "Margarite, follow me, please."

They paused just outside the door; Zielinski spoke in a low voice. "We need to keep this as quiet as possible for as long as possible. I want someone stationed out here while I let Platt know what's going on. We have to call over to the Queens North CO. Nichols didn't actually ID Kostakis as the killer, which means I still need a blanket search warrant. You'd better believe I'll get that expedited."

Holder came out of her cubicle followed by Turner. "What happened?" she asked.

"I'll fill you in." Zielinski raked his eyes over Turner. "You're free to go. Thank you for your time and assistance."

Kevin Turner looked disappointed. "I'll call you," he whispered to Holder as he left.

Zielinski turned to Holder. "Where is Carlisle, damn it? And what the hell happened to Tate?"

"I can't speak to Detective Carlisle's whereabouts, sir. Lieutenant Tate left the building. Told me to let you know she was going to get Detective Carlisle."

"What does that mean?"

"Ah, shit," Lopez responded. "She's headed to Forest Hills Gardens, to the Kostakis house. Ron—"

"Go."

Chapter 37

Dan Carlisle had trouble believing this leafy neighborhood was located within the city limits. Forest Hills Gardens was an entity unto itself, a uniquely sheltered enclave within the larger and more diverse community, protected by a century-old covenant. The homes, some of which had been standing since the 1890s, were big, at least by New York standards, and generally conformed to a Tudor-style architecture.

The neighborhood was a perfect antidote to the gritty life outside its borders. Even the weather seemed made to order. Yellow and red-leafed trees filtered bright sunshine from an azure sky. The air smelled fresh. He was tempted to walk around, take a tour of the place, fall facedown onto the emerald grass.

He would enjoy other nice days, though. The victims wouldn't.

The house where Alex and his mother lived stood on a corner lot. Large for two people unless they had live-in help. More ornate than many of its neighbors. Several old-growth trees shielded the house from the street and kept it in shadow.

His decision to head to Queens instead of back to meet with the others in Manhattan was propelled by instinct. Kostakis had taken the day off. Maybe he was visiting a chiropractor for his back. Maybe he was visiting a museum. Or maybe he was home planning his next attack.

Carlisle grabbed a cab in front of the hospital. On the way over, he Googled the Kostakis family and landed on a detailed Wikipedia page. Alexander Kostakis had grown up as the only child in a successful second-generation family. Constantine, a.k.a. Gus Kostakis, had turned his father's single grocery store into a profitable string of boutique-style food emporiums that extended across Queens, Brooklyn, and Staten Island. A fixture of the Greek community, Gus gave generously to several charities. He had died ten years earlier.

The accompanying photos showed Gus as a child and then as a grown man with his wife and son. Little Alex appeared sullen. Helena Kostakis was tall, slim, and fair-haired. She didn't appear ill; that must have occurred later.

Alex had been caring for his invalid mother for some time, according to Holder's research. Couple that with working full time while trying to change careers. What prevented him from achieving his goals? His personality, according to almost everyone that knew him. Kostakis wouldn't see it that way. Where would he direct his resentment? How would he express it?

Time to find out. He left a terse voicemail for Sam just as his phone powered down, the battery spent.

If the handsome wood door featured a bell, he couldn't locate it. Instead, he lifted a brass knocker and set off a series of chimes from inside. A middle-aged woman with coffee-colored skin answered the door. Not a maid, though. Perhaps a home health aide or a nurse.

"Can I help you?" she asked.

Carlisle had debated his opening. He began with a casual approach. "Hi. Is Alex at home?"

"He's not at the moment, Mr.—"

"Detective Dan Carlisle, Queens North Homicide. Is Mrs. Kostakis available?"

"I'm sorry, was she expecting you?"

“Please show him in, Emilia.” The voice, a pleasing alto, came from a room in the back.

Carlisle stepped into the short foyer. To his right was a stairway and a dining room, to his left, a small library. The living room straight ahead was tastefully decorated, and he could see glimpses of a garden beyond that.

“She’s in the family room,” the aide said. “Follow me.”

The open-plan kitchen seemed to be the largest area on the first floor. Carlisle, who’d picked up a couple of tips from the woman who decorated his apartment, noted the up-to-date appliances, the quartz countertop, the recessed lighting, the maple cabinets. The décor extended into the family room, which included a couch and chair in front of a large fireplace that burned even on this moderately warm day.

A woman with shoulder-length blond hair, dressed in an ice-blue sweater and black slacks, sat in a wheelchair. Her hands rested in her lap on top of a light afghan. Her silver earrings caught the light when she turned her head. She wore no obvious makeup, save a touch of gloss on her lips.

She offered her hand, her wide cornflower eyes appraising her visitor. Though she must have been in her early sixties, she appeared far younger.

Carlisle managed to keep his mouth from hanging open. He inclined his head and took the delicate hand in his. He almost bent to kiss it. She grasped it firmly, then laughed at his surprise.

“That’s quite the grip, Mrs. Kostakis.”

“You caught me on a good day, Detective,” she said. “At least a good day for this hand.” She laughed, a shimmer of silver bells. “Please call me Lena.”

She looked up at him, her direct blue gaze washing over him like cool water. He'd always been a sucker for women with extraordinary eyes and the ability to make you believe you'd been given a peek into their souls just by looking at them. He'd met three such women in the last two weeks.

He put his other hand on hers and patted it. As he'd hoped, the gesture broke the spell. She loosened her grasp, and he pulled his arm back.

"Please, sit." She pointed to the chair, which put him closer to her than the couch. He sat toward the front edge with his hands folded.

"Can I get you anything to drink, Detective?"

"No, thank you, Mrs. Kostakis." He made the decision to address her that way. He wasn't here on a social visit. "Actually, I was here to see Alex. I understand he's out. Do you know when he'll be back?"

"What is this about?"

Carlisle cleared his throat. "I don't know if you've heard about the cluster of strange homicides that have taken place recently."

"The Dry Ice Murders." She shuddered. "So awful." She put a hand to her throat. "You don't think Alex has anything to do with it?"

"He's one of many people whom the killer seems to be targeting, based on his interest in certain true crime organizations. Not that we think Alex is in any imminent danger," he added. "We're just talking with as many friends and relatives as possible to find connections."

"That makes sense." She shifted in her chair. The movement caused her to tense; he read pain in her face.

"Are you feeling okay?" he asked, rising out of his chair.

She held up a hand. "I'll be fine in a minute."

The aide appeared with a glass and a capsule Lena Kostakis popped into her mouth like candy. She chased it with a dainty gulp and let out a sigh of relief. The medicine seemed to work quickly.

"Thank you, Emilia. You can leave early today. My son will be back shortly, and I've got an NYPD detective for company."

Emilia covered her apparent doubts about Carlisle with a "yes ma'am" and turned to leave.

"Nice to meet you," he called out to the retreating figure. Then, to his hostess, "I hope you don't mind my asking, but do you suffer from MS?"

Lena Kostakis regarded him curiously. "Do you have some experience with neurological conditions, Detective?"

"My uncle had muscular dystrophy," he said, wishing he didn't have to use the past tense. "I spent some time reading about MS and similar disorders."

"Then perhaps you've heard of Guillain-Barré syndrome."

Carlisle was taken aback. "Yes, I have. It's an inflammatory disease that causes paralysis as it makes its way through the body. Horrible to get through, but I thought most people survive and the survivors generally recover with no long-lasting effects."

"That's true for most of the afflicted patients. Unfortunately, I contracted an exceedingly rare variant that has converted into a chronic condition over the past ten years. It affects me primarily in my legs, sometimes in my neck and arms. Weakness, balance problems and of course, a great deal of discomfort."

"I'm sorry to hear that. Do the doctors hold out any hope of recovery?"

She shook her head. "The doctors know nothing. They are useless when it comes to creative thinking, which is what treatment for a rare disease requires. I was misdiagnosed and, I might add, discounted for more years than I care to remember. It was Alex who discovered what really lay at the bottom of my problems. While he hasn't come upon a definitive cure, he's done a lot to ease my pain. I owe him everything."

Ease her pain or study it? Carlisle's mind raced. He would have liked to whisk this beautiful woman out of her gilded cage and over to a top-notch neurologist. Right now, though, he needed to stay on track.

"You're lucky to have a son like that," he said. "Too bad your husband isn't around to see how well he's done for himself."

She let out a small sigh filled with regret. "Yes, that might have been helpful to Alex, assuming Constantine was capable of change. He was hard on the boy. Stingy with praise, generous with criticism that took the form of insult. Claimed it would toughen Alex up. Mind you, there was nothing weak about my son. He was, if anything, headstrong like my husband. And he loved his father, insofar as he could love."

"That's an odd statement to make about a child, isn't it?"

"I suppose it is. Then again, Alex was odd to many people. Less social, more introverted, very introspective. Fascinated by details. I can understand why he turned to true crime as a hobby. He approaches these cases as if they were puzzles. He revels in the minutia, some might say. I find that people who combine an interest in detail with an unlimited imagination end up creating unique solutions."

Or uniquely horrible deaths, Carlisle thought to himself. "The medical profession sounds like a good fit," he said.

"Perhaps. I always thought he might be better off in a laboratory. Less interaction, more time for discovery. But Alex was determined to become a doctor and earn his father's respect."

"Was that important to Alex? To be respected by his father?"

"I think that's every young man's goal, don't you, Detective Carlisle? I will say that the concept of respect was vitally important to his father. It may have been tied to his upbringing. His own father came to this country with nothing and became a revered member of the Greek community in Queens."

She shook her head. "Constantine lectured constantly on respect and reputation. You work for it; you earn it. And when you finally get it, you fight like hell to keep it. Alex may have"—she struggled for words—"taken that to mean something a bit different. For him, respect was active and alive, a thing with a clear opposite."

"Disrespect," Carlisle suggested.

"Disrespect, yes, but it was also broader than that. In Alex's world, disinterest is a sign of disrespect. Inattention is a sign of disrespect. Rejection is a sign of disrespect."

"I should tell you that a few of Alex's colleagues feel that his behavior toward them reflects that approach. He comes across as dismissive."

"You've talked to his colleagues."

"We've talked to family, friends, and colleagues of everyone who may have interacted with the killer as part of a routine investigation," Carlisle replied.

"I see. Well, if Alex comes across that way, it's purely defensive. If his father wasn't irritated, he was indifferent. In school, if his classmates weren't teasing him, they were giving him the cold shoulder."

The back of Carlisle's neck prickled. "Cold shoulder," he said almost conversationally.

"Yes. To him, being ignored or being given the cold shoulder was the ultimate sign of disrespect." She laughed.

Carlisle recalled Sam quoting Death of a Salesman: "Attention must be paid."

The woman in front of him smiled, then suddenly began to topple from her chair. He jumped up to catch her in his arms and felt a sharp pain in his neck.

He reached up to swat away whatever the hell had stung or bitten him. His arm froze halfway there and fell helplessly back down. His legs gave way, and he crumbled to the floor at the feet of the woman he'd been trying to help, his vision blurred.

Listen, he commanded himself, but heard only the labored breathing of the woman in the wheelchair, then his own heartbeat, then nothing.

Chapter 38

Carlisle's voicemail sent Sam out of the conference room. She didn't need to be present for the paperwork that would precede any action. She needed to get to Danny Carlisle, who was an idiot for not picking up when she called. And for heading into a dangerous situation without backup.

For that matter, so was she. But at least she had Dimitri.

She'd texted her aunt's enigmatic friend as soon as she realized Danny was heading to Queens. Dimitri told her he could have a car and driver waiting for her in two minutes. That put her at least ten minutes ahead of Lopez—or maybe they'd all arrive at the same time. Two's company, three's a crowd, but also insurance.

A Lincoln Town Car waited outside the precinct, its motor purring like a confident cat. The man who stood by the back door was bald, his face hollowed out like a skull. He was well over six feet and so thin Sam thought he might topple over. As she drew near, she revised her impression. He looked more like a steel rod than a tender sapling.

"I am Vlad," he said, inclining his large head. He handed her a card like the one Dimitri had given her. "Please check your phone."

Surprised, Sam looked at her cell and saw a familiar number attached to a brief text.

Vlad is picking you up. He's okay. Xoxo Rosa

She couldn't help it; she laughed out loud. Either her aunt watched too many detective shows, or Sam was living inside one right now.

She clambered into the spacious back seat. Vlad strode over to the driver's side and started moving almost before he got his stringy body inside.

"Where are we going?" he asked.

She gave him the address in Forest Hills Gardens and sat back, only to jerk forward when he stuck a mobile flasher on the dashboard.

"That looks like police issue," she remarked.

"You are on police business," Vlad replied, and that was the end of that.

Ten minutes into the trip, Sam remembered she'd left her gun in her aunt's house. She couldn't waste time and energy berating herself; she needed to make do. She reached into a compartment of her now-favorite leather bag. Her hand wrapped around a small container of pepper spray combined with CS tear gas, a formulation available only to police officers. That would be effective in a close-up situation. The adjacent pocket held her beloved Swiss Army knife. Beloved because the model she had contained every kind of tool imaginable, including a potentially lethal blade.

Moving to the main compartment, she discovered a couple of zip ties. Then bumped into the folded black cane. She'd put it in her purse to see whether she could walk without it. The answer turned out to be "more or less."

She shook it open and moved it around, testing its weight and efficacy as a weapon. Suddenly, she had an image of Stefan in a *gi* tied with a brown belt. He started martial arts lessons the year she was born, which was also when he saw *The Karate Kid*, starring Ralph Macchio and Pat Morita. For several years, he practiced diligently.

Sam's father took her to a demonstration in which Stefan and his classmates engaged in stick fighting, or *bōjutsu*. She might have been five, which put her brother into his senior year of high school. Everything about the performance thrilled her, from the formalized, almost reverent introduction to the power that seemed to come from a single thrust. At home she tried to imitate the moves with a broom and a high-pitched yell. She nearly put her eye out. That was it, as far as her mother was concerned.

"Let her take lessons, Ma," Stefan had implored. "Lots of girls are doing karate. Some of them are really good at it. It's great self-defense and it instills discipline." He gave his mother his best smile, one she could never resist.

"When she's ten," her mother conceded. "Not before."

Ten years old never came, at least not in the way Sophia Russo had imagined. Years later, Sam Tate would pick up the *bō* as part of her army training and find she had a knack for stick fighting. Not Ralph Macchio–level skills but good enough. She embraced the ritual and the structure. She even managed to absorb some of the more practical aspects of the Eastern religions that influenced the practice, like dedicating oneself to becoming a better being. Survivor's guilt played a part in her desire to become new and improved, as did the ray of hope that doing so would make her feel better.

Unfortunately, that was more than a decade ago, and though she was still agile enough, she had the foot injury to contend with. She had no idea what she'd be able to handle if it came to that.

But you will handle it, she told herself.

She swished the cane through the air a few times and nodded. In the rearview mirror, she caught Vlad's quizzical gaze. She shrugged. If his Lincoln could impersonate a police vehicle, she could impersonate a brown belt. Minus the kicks.

Vlad made good time. He stopped the car down the block from the Kostakis house and killed the engine just as Sam caught the text from Lopez. Something about being stuck in traffic, along with a question about Carlisle's whereabouts.

The frustration encapsulated by the few words pulled Sam in several directions. On one hand, she'd gone off without informing anyone of her whereabouts. Impulsive behavior, notwithstanding her good intentions. On the other hand, she felt the pressure of rising to the demands of her job, of being there as needed. Not a great excuse but the only one she had. That and a gut feeling.

If Danny was having a nice chat with Mrs. Kostakis, she'd simply become a part of it. If something else were going on, she had her trusty cane as well as a couple of zip-ties she always carried. Either way, she would respond to Lopez as soon as she'd assessed the situation.

She shut off her phone.

Vlad popped out of the car and opened the door. Sam extricated herself from the back seat. She gave an *oof* as her weight landed on her right foot. At least she'd been able to squeeze into a pair of shoes, which offered slightly more protection. At least her foot was bruised, not shot up.

That brought a grim smile to her face.

"Are you okay?" Vlad asked. "I could stay, in case you needed anything."

Sam had no doubt he could provide a variety of services. His hands were callused, the knuckles enlarged. She didn't think he got the nasty-looking scar slightly below his jawline from shaving.

"Thank you, Vlad. I'm just going to join my partner on an interview."

He swiveled his head from side to side as if looking for danger. He then reached inside the car and under the driver's seat. "At least you must take this," he said.

"This" turned out to be a SIG Sauer P365, an efficient and popular lightweight gun favored by the concealed carry crowd. He held the weapon out to her with great formality, as if it were a sacred offering.

"Don't worry," Vlad said. "Is legal and registered." His face remained impassive.

"Vlad," she began. She couldn't figure out how to deal with his offer.

"Just for safety," he added.

"Why don't you hold onto it?" she suggested. "I promise to call you for backup if I need help."

"You will use stick?" he asked in disbelief.

"I will be fine. I appreciate the gesture, believe me. I promise to call if I need help. Thank you and please thank Dimitri."

"You have number," Vlad said. He got back into the car and drove away.

Chapter 39

"I've been stuck in traffic for half an hour!" Lopez yelled through the phone. She threw in an impressive string of epitaphs for good measure. "Where are you?"

"I'm still at the home office." Zielinski answered. "I've got the warrants. What happened?"

"I was at the Queens–Midtown Tunnel in ten minutes. Then this a-hole driver jams his clearly oversized tractor trailer into the entrance. Right in front of me. I'm watching him make his move and yelling at the top of my lungs, but of course he can't hear me. No, he goes and gets himself stuck."

"You're not inside the tunnel, are you?" Zielinski had very few phobias, but he knew for a fact he would hate to be stalled in a tunnel that ran several miles underwater.

"No, for all the good that does me. I'm sandwiched between the jammed-up rig and a bus. I hit the siren, which got the bus driver's attention. At least he's trying to back up to give me some space to turn around, but he's got a dozen idiots on his tail. It's like being in a freaking parking lot. Did you hear from Danny or Sam?"

"No," Zielinski replied. "Carlisle's been there less than an hour. Hopefully not enough time to get into trouble. And if Sam is right behind him ..." He let the thought drop. "The warrants mean we can call in the cops from the precinct nearest the house."

"That's a backup plan if I don't get through in the next five minutes."

"I can light a fire under the traffic cops if you think it'll help. They already know me because of my tendency to treat orange stoplights as if they were green." He was trying to keep it light, keep the rising concern he felt to himself.

"Anything will help. I just need to know if I can get through this mess or if I gotta turn around."

"Don't turn back, Lopez. Crawl over bumpers, hitch a ride with the traffic cops, push the cars through the tunnel if you have to. Whatever it takes to get across. I'll see about clearing a path on 495."

She let a beat go by. "You're worried," she stated flatly.

"I'm trying to account for all the possibilities. Keep your phone charged and keep me updated on your position. Meanwhile, I'll call Danny's CO."

So much for sounding unconcerned, he thought as he clicked off.

He looked up to find Holder standing at his desk.

"I don't suppose Lieutenant Tate got in touch with you?" he asked.

"No, and I haven't been able to reach her. Her phone's GPS doesn't seem to be working, either."

Zielinski allowed himself a short and pungent profanity, which he accompanied by a fist slam to the desk that caused his mug to jump. Holder startled at his uncommon reaction.

"Sorry. This day is getting complicated. Okay, what do you have for me? I assume that's why you're here. Make it quick, Officer. I need to get Detective Lopez out of a jam—literally—and then call for reinforcements from across the river."

Holder pushed her glasses up her nose and consulted her tablet. "I dug up juvenile records on Alex

Kostakis," she began. "Which, I know, are technically sealed and thus inadmissible."

"We'll deal with that later. I want to know what you found. Strictly as background."

"Alex Kostakis was arrested for animal abuse following a half dozen complaints from neighbors whose pets had gone missing. Mostly cats, along with one dog."

"Don't tell me. Young Alex 'borrowed' them for some sort of science project."

"Yup. He tortured the animals, monitored them to see how they reacted to the pain, then dissected them to see what the torture had done to them. Recorded everything on video in a little basement lab his parents built for him. They claimed they had no idea what he was up to. I guess that's code for 'we weren't really paying attention.'"

Zielinski felt his bile rise. He'd seen a lot of depravity over the years. Nothing infuriated him more than cruelty, especially when used on innocents like children or pets. Then again, not all children were innocent.

"How old was he when this went down?"

Holder didn't need her notes. "Ten when he started, thirteen when they caught him."

"And?"

"He went before a judge in juvenile court just before New York passed the law that classifies severe animal cruelty as a felony. His parents received a fine. The judge assigned a pediatric psychiatrist to interview Alex, but the boy's father retained his own behavioral specialist."

"Let me guess. Alex had no idea what he did was wrong."

Holder grimaced. “The two agreed on that much. The boy claimed he was using animals for testing purposes, just like big companies did. Anyway, the real disagreement was over rehabilitation. The court shrink was worried; the family therapist thought Alex just needed a little more time under the loving and watchful supervision of his parents.”

“That was it? No more incidents?”

“None that I could find. According to the court reports, Alex was kept on a very short leash in high school. He was allowed to join the science club and the swim team. Nothing else. No parties or dances, only events connected with church. His family hired an adult companion who was always with Alex except when the boy was in class or with his parents.”

“A kind of jail, then. And an opportunity to feed a sense of injustice.”

“Right, although the boy insisted that he wasn’t angry, only curious as to why his work was misunderstood.” She shook her head. “One more thing. Alex Kostakis tortured the poor kitties by shoving dry ice down their little throats.”

“That’s pretty damn specific. Good work, Officer.”

A text popped up from Lopez.

I'm thru. Less than ten min out

Zielinski exhaled. He typed back:

Be careful. It's definitely Kostakis

No shit, she typed. E-fax warrants and send me backup

No doubt about it, Zielinski thought. Alex Kostakis was their killer. Neither did he doubt that Detective Dan Carlisle had walked himself into a dangerous situation. He only hoped that Sam Tate hadn’t followed him all the way in.

Chapter 40

Sam stood in the quiet that followed Vlad's departure. She heard only birdsong and the soft rustle of leaves. The Kostakis residence reminded her of a small castle, lacking only a stone wall to ward off invading armies. The unattached single-car garage was closed. No vehicles were parked in front of the house or in the driveway. Danny had arrived by cab.

She walked around to the side, listening for the bark of a dog or a query from a neighbor. A locked, wrought-iron fence led to a small backyard with a patch of lawn ringed by several neat little gardens. The space was dominated by a stone patio with a blue-striped awning. Behind it, two sliding doors led back into the house, possibly to the kitchen and a den.

She returned to the front door and lifted the knocker. A bell chimed; the tune was reminiscent of Big Ben. She waited several beats and sent the sonorous notes through the house once more. Then she reached instinctively to the handle below and found, to her surprise, that the door was unlocked.

"Good afternoon," she called out. "I'm Detective Sam Tate, here to join my partner, Detective Danny Carlisle." She'd rehearsed her opening lines on the way over, afraid she might inadvertently introduce herself as "lieutenant" or "sheriff."

"Hello?" she tried again as she moved down a short hallway. The house was laid out to accommodate a relatively narrow footprint, although Sam assumed renovations had been made over time. She moved past a couple of small, dark rooms and into the kitchen. The mix of warm wood, stone, and high-end appliances reminded Sam more of an upscale country home than a baroque villa. She didn't cook much, but after seeing Carlisle's apartment and now this, she wondered how she could go back to her mix-and-match scullery.

Like so many other houses built for show, the room farthest from the front door looked the coziest. The space seemed both roomy and intimate. And warm, probably owing to the switched-on gas fireplace.

Who spent time here? She doubted the busy, possibly homicidal son sat and read by the fire. The mother, a woman who, according to Holder's report, suffered from an undisclosed malady. She looked down and saw the faint imprint of twin wheels on the area rug. Helena Kostakis was confined to a wheelchair.

The cushion of the chair next to the couch bore an indentation. Someone had been sitting here recently. A nurse? Carlisle? Sam set down her cane and bag, then crouched, careful to keep one leg behind her. The position was awkward but took weight off the bad foot.

Squinting, she picked up a trail made by the wheelchair that led off the area rug and onto the hardwood floor. She let her eyes follow an imagined path to one side of the fireplace. The simple yet classic wood mantle was painted white. It extended several feet on either side and blended seamlessly with the wall. Or maybe not.

She went for a closer look. A tap on the wood and presto! A panel slid to one side to reveal a small elevator, just big enough for a wheelchair and two occupants, one standing. This was apparently how Mrs. Kostakis reached the upper floors. Clever.

She came back to the chair and thought about her next move. Mrs. Kostakis could be upstairs. Maybe Danny helped her or maybe a home-health aide. Surely Helena Kostakis could afford one.

A gleam by the corner of the sofa caught her eye. She stooped to retrieve a small object half-hidden by the fabric skirt and closed her hand around a gold pin in the shape of a horn.

Danny had been here, which begged the question: Where was he now?

Sam's heart began to pump. She would need the adrenaline, but not yet. She slowed her breathing and directed her attention to the rug again. If Danny walked or had been moved from the scene, maybe the accommodating rug could provide a clue.

The flat weave seemed unwilling to give up any more information. The bare floor was another matter. Sam located a small black scuff mark. Now she saw the door in the corner of the room. Not hidden, just unobtrusive. Plain white, brass knob. A linen closet, perhaps, or a powder room.

Sam pulled her jacket over her hand and gently turned the handle. The door opened onto a set of stairs leading down. She descended to a lower level made entirely of brick and stone, like a medieval warren with a fully stocked wine cellar behind an archway.

She made her way down a narrow corridor clutching her cane and passed a laundry room, a storage room, and a utility room, all windowless, all encased in stone. The passageway led to a space that seemed two parts government laboratory and one part hobbyist.

It was as if two set pieces occupied one stage. In the center between them sat a reclining chair like those found in a dentist office. Danny Carlisle had been strapped in, conscious but clearly unable to move. He stared at her, eyes wide open in fear.

Sam forced herself to stay still. She pulled her eyes off the terrified man and swept the room.

The lab section was comprised of neat shelves that held a variety of bottles, a glass-front refrigerator, a metal table, several pieces of expensive-looking equipment, and fluorescent lighting.

A second area was designed more like a dorm room. A lumpy-looking couch held a pillow and blanket and might have doubled as a bed. An overflowing bookcase made of cheap wood stood in one corner, a simple writing desk in another. The old-fashioned reading lamp by the patched armchair was switched off. Sam wasn't surprised to see a blood red shag area rug on the floor.

Alex Kostakis turned from the metal table with a smile, as if she'd just caught him in the middle of an experiment. He wore disposable slip-ons over sandals and a pair of heavy-duty gloves. In his hands was a pair of tongs. Empty for now, but Sam saw a large cooler under the table.

"Why, hello, Lieutenant, how nice of you to join us. Did you know you're the third law officer to see my lab in the space of a month?"

"I do now."

He glanced at her cane. "How's your foot coming along? Mine is going to take a while. That doesn't make me happy, but we must soldier on."

Sam's brain was issuing commands at warp speed. *Stay calm. Assess the situation. Keep the suspect talking. Find his weak spot. Find your opening.*

She forced herself to look not at Carlisle but at his tormentor.

"Hello, Alex. I didn't see your mother when I came in. Is she down here with you? Does she know about your nasty hobby? Does she collaborate with you, or is she one of your subjects?"

"PA Kostakis, Lieutenant," he scolded. "I won't remind you again. My mother is resting in the master bedroom on the second floor. She's not well, as you may have guessed. I'm surprised you didn't check. You probably wanted to locate your partner. As you can see, he's indisposed at the moment." He inclined his head to the chair.

"He looks uncomfortable."

Kostakis chuckled. "Far from it. He is as relaxed as he's ever likely to be. He is, in fact, the first to try my most sophisticated hybrid paralytic. Unlike with the previous subjects, his immobility skirts the esophagus and the diaphragm entirely. He can swallow! He can breathe! No more dislocated jaws or ventilators."

He grinned like a boy who'd won first prize at the science fair.

"But you still plan to hurt him," Sam said.

Kostakis scowled. "I don't enjoy inflicting pain, Lieutenant. I enjoy studying it. A distinction you fail to grasp."

"What's the goal, Alex? Do you have some humanitarian endgame in mind or a plan to end suffering instead of causing it? I somehow doubt it. You seem to be all about making a statement. You literally ice people for the crime of ignoring you. Your response to the proverbial cold shoulder. Were your victims guilty or were they stand-ins for a lifetime of insult?"

The pupils in his icy eyes shrunk to pinpoints. She'd struck a nerve.

"Coming back to the scene of the crime as an MLI was diabolical," she continued. "Definitely one for the serial killer books."

"I'm a scientist, not a serial killer," Kostakis answered, his tone sharp. "An innovator. And not as gullible as you seem to think I am. No, no."

He waggled his finger at her. "I'm not affected by your attempts at analysis. I don't care what you say. You will die along with Detective Carlisle, and that's on you. The passageway you used to locate me has been locked. I have the means to flood this space with CO2 and a secret exit you'll never locate."

Sam took a step. Kostakis bent to the cooler and plucked out a piece of solid CO2 with his tongs. He held it over Carlisle's face. "Don't move, Lieutenant. I can still kill your friend the slow and tortuous way."

Carlisle suddenly jerked forward from the chair, his left shoulder hitting Kostakis in the back and causing him to stumble. He dropped the tongs; the ice hit the floor with a sizzle. Sam swung her cane, intending to hit him midsection. Her blow landed well below the kneecap.

The resulting crack vibrated back through her hands and wrists and nearly knocked her over. She'd hit not bone but metal. Kostakis was using a support brace, probably to take the weight off his foot.

Her blow still hurt; she could tell. Even better, it made him angry.

"Bitch!" he shrieked and lurched forward on his good leg.

Sam drove the stick down like a spear, straight through his sock and into the tender part of his foot. She twisted it, then pulled it out. Kostakis howled like an animal. He stumbled and fell onto his back. From the floor, he tried to kick at her with his uninjured leg. She tromped on his kneecap and felt something snap. More screaming, which she ignored.

She dropped her knees to either side of his torso, sitting on his abdomen above his useless legs and pinning his arms. She lifted the cane above her head like a sword. She could end him, thrust her weapon into his excuse for a heart. Or cut away at him little by little. How many wounds for how many deaths? How much pain for how much suffering? How much blood to stain the bare floor until it turned as red as the horrible rug nearby?

"Sam." She heard the effort that single word cost Carlisle. Did he want to remind her that behind the avenging warrior prepared to pierce the heart of her enemy lay a good cop, a dedicated cop, a decent human being?

She wrestled with her rage. *There is no justice but mine,* she imagined yelling, except she didn't believe it. The man she sat astride had to pay, without a doubt. The system in place to do that, however imperfect, was the one she was sworn to uphold.

Sam didn't move at all for six long seconds. Finally, she stood and in one fluid motion flipped Kostakis over onto his stomach and zip-tied him. He yelped.

She squatted by his head and hissed into his ear. "If you move an inch or utter a sound, I will impale you. Do you understand?"

He managed to nod.

Sam stepped over him and reached for Carlisle, who had slid down in the chair. She undid the binding and pulled him onto the floor. With his head in her lap, she examined him for wounds. No burning around the mouth, just a small blister on his cheek.

Carlisle struggled to speak.

"You don't need to talk right now, Danny. Use your eyes. One blink for yes, two blinks for no. First, did you swallow any dry ice? Can you move? Wait, can you blink?"

Two blinks, two more, and one slow one. She started to giggle, looked down to see the corner of his mouth lift. She couldn't help it; she threw her head back and roared with laughter.

Chapter 41

"I honestly thought you'd lost your mind," Lopez told Sam.

The two of them were sitting in the visitors lounge on the third floor of New York Presbyterian–Queens. Sam had an ice pack tied to her foot, which rested on a small stool provided by a sympathetic nurse. Danny Carlisle's room was down the hall. The door was closed to outsiders while a team of doctors examined him. A half dozen detectives milled about the hall, including Carlisle's CO and the assistant chief of detectives.

It occurred to Sam that she'd now visited three different hospitals in the space of two weeks. Not exactly a routine New York holiday. Then again, neither was catching a serial killer.

Lopez had breached the underground lair with help from a tactical team from the 112th. They took down the locked door using a twelve-gauge projectile. When they burst through, they found their primary suspect facedown, hands secured behind him, one foot bleeding, the other bent at an odd angle. The female subject, immediately identified as a "friendly," was sitting cross-legged on the floor with another man's head in her lap, laughing, as one officer said later, "like a crazy woman."

The team found several canisters believed to contain CO2 on an interconnected timing device, Lopez reported. They located the second exit behind a false wall inside what appeared to be a closet. A set of wooden stairs led outside. In the refrigerator unit, they gathered up various serums that Lopez hoped might tie back to the drugs found in the victims' systems.

They also found Mrs. Kostakis upstairs in her wheelchair in a locked room. She was brought to the same hospital and was undergoing both a physical and psychological evaluation.

"The doctors want to see if her paralysis was caused by a kind of nerve-blocking injection, since Alex seems to have a fondness for sticking people with syringes filled with drugs they didn't ask for," Lopez said. "Can you imagine?"

Sam could not.

Helen Kostakis faced other problems. Ten years of neuromuscular injections, even one customized to affect only certain parts of the body, could have created permanent organ damage. A decade of muscle atrophy might mean she would never regain use of certain limbs.

Then there was the issue of what she knew, what she ignored, and how complicit that made her in her son's activities.

An imposing woman wearing a uniform with plenty of brass stepped into the waiting area. She carried her hat under one arm, military style.

Lopez sprang out of her chair and Sam followed suit, ignoring the ice pack that slipped to the floor.

"Assistant Chief Vanessa Ortiz, I'm Margarite Lopez, Manhattan North Homicide. And this is our special consultant, Lieutenant Sam Tate."

"I know who both of you are," the assistant chief replied with a wide smile. "Lieutenant Tate, how is your foot?"

"Better, ma'am, thank you."

"Good. I want to update you on your colleague. All good news, I'm happy to report. Detective Carlisle will not require surgery. Nor does it seem he ingested any dry ice. He has a bump on the head and bruises from being dragged down a flight of stairs and across a rough surface. He also has a burn on his face that will heal."

"What about the paralytic?" Sam asked.

"It seems to be wearing off," Ortiz replied. "Detective Carlisle will need to remain under observation for at least twenty-four hours. The doctors think Kostakis modified a transient neuromuscular inhibitor commonly used for surgery."

"Something he could get from work," Sam observed.

"Does that mean his victims weren't unconscious?" Lopez clenched her fists.

"We don't know what it means yet, Detective Lopez. This drug needs to be analyzed and compared with the toxins found in the victims. The lab techs also need to examine the vials recovered from the basement and the one in the bedroom where Mrs. Kostakis was found. They have their work cut out for them."

"Where is Kostakis?" Sam asked.

"Here in the hospital, under lock and key. He's got a broken kneecap on one leg, and two different wounds in his other foot that have led to an infection." She focused on Sam. "These were administered, as I understand, by a walking stick."

"Yes ma'am," Lopez piped up.

"He won't be mobile anytime soon, but of course, no one trusts him. We've got uniforms outside his hospital room. The ADA is moving to expedite a hearing. Given the publicity, it could happen very soon. Quite a few of Detective Carlisle's fellow officers would like a turn at Kostakis, and I don't mean standing guard. Not that I'd allow anything to happen, but I understand the temptation."

Sam nodded. At least she'd worked out some of her wrath on the suspect.

"What about Chloe Nichols?" Lopez asked.

"Internal Affairs will meet on her case this evening. Both the Manhattan and Queens offices are likely to be present."

"Who will represent Nichols?"

Ortiz considered Sam's question. "Her union will provide representation. For your information, her problems are well-documented, as is her previously exemplary record. I don't know what her future holds, but if rehabilitation is an option, it will be offered."

"Thank you for letting me know," Sam said.

Lopez caught sight of Zielinski and waved him over.

"Detectives," he said. "I assume Assistant Chief Ortiz has you all caught up?"

"She does," Sam replied.

The assistant chief smiled broadly. "Detective Sergeant Zielinski, congratulations on your promotion."

"Thank you, ma'am."

"Your CO and I will want to debrief you and your team. She and I will set that up along with the CO for Queens North Homicide. I don't need to tell you that all media inquiries should be directed to the Office of the Chief of Detectives. We're coordinating a response with the mayor's team. There'll be a press conference. This is a win, but there will be questions."

"I think Lieutenant Tate is used to dodging media inquiries," Lopez said with a straight face. Sam stifled the urge to poke her friend in the arm.

"I'm sure she is. By the way, Lieutenant, you're cleared to go in to see Detective Carlisle. I imagine he wants to thank you for saving his life." Ortiz chuckled as she walked back down the hall.

"I'm in the presence of greatness," Lopez wisecracked.

"You're part of it, Margarite," Zielinski said. "We've all earned a pat on the back. Although I might have something to say about special consultants who run off without informing their team."

Sam swallowed and bent down to pick up her ice pack.

"Come on, Zielinski," Lopez said. "Sam subdued the suspect with a cane. No shots fired."

Sam flashed on herself sitting astride Alex Kostakis, arms stretched over head, prepared to drive a pointed stick into and through his heart. What if Lopez and the others had burst upon that scene? Would she now be sitting in a room waiting to be evaluated like poor Helena Kostakis?

"I was downstairs when they brought Kostakis in." Zielinski was watching Sam closely. "His foot looked bloody awful, pardon the pun. You did that with a cane?"

Sam shrugged. "I hit soft tissue." She glanced down the hall. "Let me go check on Danny."

She slipped on her mask and walked over to Carlisle's room. The group outside his door crowded around her with backslaps and high fives and "atta girls." One man called out, "Tennessee tough." Another followed with "Watch out; the sheriff is in town." Everybody laughed, then stepped back to let her slip through the door and lock it.

"Someone sure is popular."

Carlisle was propped up in bed wearing a hospital gown someone had haphazardly tied around him. Despite a monitor and a couple of IV drips, he looked chipper, albeit drained.

Sam laughed. She walked over to the bed and smiled at him. "That someone is you. Your colleagues out there are celebrating your survival. They're also vowing to make sure someone has an eye on Kostakis until they send him wherever they're going to send him."

"Probably Attica," Carlisle replied. "Is he on suicide watch?"

"I can't see someone like him ending his life. He's too fond of himself."

"What about Chloe?"

"I was told Internal Affairs is going to decide how to proceed with input from both district attorneys. I have the impression they'll take her problems into consideration. But there will be consequences."

"I know." He reached out and grabbed her hand.

She waited for the spark or, more significantly, a deeper connection. What washed over her was relief at seeing a valued colleague on the mend and affection for a dear friend. Nothing more.

He felt it too, a shift in the air. He released her arm. "My upper body reflexes are returning," he said with a nod.

"How about your legs? Can you move them?"

"I have some sensation. Doctors are pretty sure it'll all come back to me. I'll be chasing bad guys in no time. Or bad girls," he added with a smile.

"I don't think you'll want for opportunity."

Carlisle bit his lip. "You're an extraordinary woman, you know."

"Danny—"

"Let me finish, Tate. Not just your looks, although you are awesomely beautiful, as the kids might say. And not just your physical strength, although I don't think I'll ever meet anyone, male or female, who can lift an overhead steel door with her toes or handle a walking stick like it was a samurai sword."

Sam flushed. "You can never tell anyone."

"I never would. I like the idea of having a couple of secrets between us." He took her hand. "We were crushing on each other for a minute, weren't we?"

"We were," she said softly.

"I expect you to do great things, Tate. Not in New York. Not now, at any rate. Also not in Eastern Maryland, and that's me speaking as a friend."

"How about Washington, DC? I have a job offer. Hush-hush for now. Advancement possibilities. I think I'm going to take it."

"Washington. More politics, not less. But you can keep an eye on your senator. And maybe close the distance on a certain relationship."

Sam looked at their intertwined hands; he let go.

"Just so you know, and I'm still speaking as a friend, if you ever need anything, you reach out to me from wherever you are. I'll be there in a flash. It's the least I can do for someone who speared a suspect to save my life."

"I heart you, Dan Carlisle," Sam said and kissed him gently on the forehead.

"Take a number, Tate." He waved, then turned his head away.

Sam walked out the door and into an empty passageway. The assembled well-wishers had moved on.

Good. She needed a moment to collect herself. She took several slow, deep breaths and shook herself. Carlisle was going to be okay. And so was she.

From the visitors lounge, she heard someone call her name.

"Hey, Tate, Detective Lopez has been filling me in on your so-called vacation. You got any pictures we can post to Instagram?"

She tore down the hallway and threw herself into Terry Sloane's waiting arms. He didn't flinch against the onslaught but caught her in a wordless embrace. She buried her face in his solid, familiar chest and let the tears flow.

Epilogue

"Senator Parker is here, sir." The stylish, black-suited woman spoke into the phone, received her reply, and rose from her desk. "Right this way, Senator," she said.

Sean Parker followed her down a short corridor filled with artwork and living plants. Recessed fixtures added a glow that was supplemented by the natural light from a skylight. Someone had strung fairy lights, perhaps as a nod to the holiday season.

At the end of the hallway, the woman entered a numerical series onto a discreet keypad. This activated a sliding door that lay flat against the wall, nearly invisible to the casual observer. It opened onto a beautifully appointed office with what appeared to be customized furniture. The floor-to-ceiling windows afforded a panoramic view of downtown Providence. As soon as Parker entered, the woman disappeared.

A slope-shouldered, white-haired man in a cashmere jacket stood at the window. When he turned around, Parker couldn't help but notice the deep furrows that ran along the sides of his face and the excess skin that hung from his chin almost to his chest.

"You look well, Joseph," Parker said by way of greeting.

"What, no Uncle Joe?" the old man replied. "I suppose you're used to more formality these days, Senator."

He smiled, his sparkling dentures at odds with his aged visage. Though in his early nineties, his voice hadn't changed. Deep, sonorous, controlled, persuasive. A purr that could without warning become a roar. A voice that had once advised powerful men, seduced women, commanded subordinates, and intimidated so many others, including Parker himself.

"This"—Parker indicated his surroundings—"is quite the setup."

"Isn't it? My son is all about sustainable living. Systems, materials, the chair you sit on, the clothes you wear, the car you drive, the food you eat. Most of what you see is made of bamboo or some other natural matter that isn't likely to disappear in ten years. Radiant heat, recycled air. I can't keep track. All I know is he makes a fortune. He's got me sitting on the board of his company, where I don't do a damn thing to earn this gorgeous office."

A wet cough interrupted his train of thought. "Sorry. Healthy living hasn't brought back my lungs, even though I gave up cigars years ago. At least I'm still here. Speaking of which, I was sorry to hear about your father."

"Thanks. It was his time."

"Glad he died in the comfort of his own home instead of in a damned prison cell." He gestured to a comfortable chair and took a seat behind the desk. "Have a seat."

Parker hesitated, then sat.

"How's your mother doing, by the way?"

"She's fine, thanks. I've moved her to an assisted living facility in Maryland."

"You were always a good son to your parents. Made us all proud." He winked, an animated skull in an expensive jacket.

"I had help."

"We got you started. You did the rest. By the way, congratulations are in order. First you get elected to the Senate. Then you get engaged to that media heiress. She's a lawyer, isn't she?"

"That's right."

"Smart, good-looking, connected, and rich. Locked and loaded. When's the wedding?"

Parker didn't answer.

"Smile, Sean. You have it all. Money, power, a great woman, more on the side if that's what you decide you want."

"I only ever wanted the one, Joseph."

"A youthful mistake. Best nipped in the bud, so to speak." He took in Parker's stiff posture. "Is that why you're still so angry? The girl? Or is this about what happened in Queens?"

"Why does it have to be one or the other? You destroyed my chance at happiness. Then you ordered me to destroy my sister's happiness."

"Half-sister," the old man replied. "A woman you didn't even know. Your job was to deliver a message to her husband on behalf of the family."

"At a wedding. With a gun. Like I was some sort of hired assassin."

"Was the assignment too low rent for you, Sean? Did you use your weapon? I read the transcripts, you know. The kid was fixated on a man with a brown suit she thinks pulled a gun."

"Brown was a popular color for men back in the nineties," Parker said.

"Enigmatic as usual. Makes me wonder if you were even there."

The old man placed his hands on the desk. Carefully manicured, though spotted with age, they still looked capable, strong. Parker knew he'd been the well-educated counselor to the Patriarca family. Maybe his usefulness hadn't been confined to advice.

"Here's the bottom line, Sean. It's ancient history. No need to keep bringing it up. Past time for you to let all that go."

"Is it, though? Then what's your interest after all these years?"

"I might ask you the same thing," the old man snapped. "How come you connected with that girl, that half-niece, after all this time? She's working and living in DC, thanks to you. With a senior FBI type, no less. Why would you want to make that happen?"

"Maybe I want to keep an eye on her."

"Why? You think she's going to stumble onto something? Does she even know you're her half uncle?"

"No," Parker lied.

"Good. Let's keep it that way. I heard the mother just died. That's a blessing in more ways than one. Look, Sam Tate is free and clear. She's got a new name, a new job, a steady boyfriend. This would be an ideal time for her to turn the page on her past."

"Just stay away from her," Parker said.

The old man laughed. "Either you're getting sentimental, and I don't believe that for a minute, or you've got another angle."

Parker stood. "My interest in or feelings about Sam are none of your concern. I have my own plans. You don't need to know what they are, and I don't need either approval or input from you or any of your associates."

Instead of responding, the old man reached into his pocket and withdrew an electronic cigarette. "Someone told me this, what do they call it, vaping is better for me," he said. "Piece of crap plastic, probably made in China. Like something my granddaughter would use." He pulled, exhaled with satisfaction. "Ah, well. We all gotta make sacrifices, right?"

He looked up and squinted at Parker. "Sit down, Sean, and let me offer you a piece of advice. Don't bite the hand that feeds you, son. You're in the catbird seat right now, but we can still ..."

"You can still what, Joseph? Get me to do your bidding? I don't think so."

The old man coughed, once, then again. He dropped the vape and waved a hand in front of his face as if to ward off evil spirits. The coughing turned into choking. He pounded his chest and fell back in his chair. "The cigarette," he gasped.

"Consider it enhanced. Call it modern technology or bio-weaponry. A hard-to-trace poison, designed to shred lungs. Mix in a little help from outsiders and money spent in the right places and offered to the right people. There's more than one way to persuade people to do your bidding, Joseph. Although force has its place."

Parker came around the desk and stood over the man who had governed his life for many years.

"Listen up, old man. Blood doesn't matter. Background doesn't matter. Loyalty is conditional. What counts now is power and influence. For instance, I'm now in a position to grind the entire *familia* into dust with the help of my new friends at the FBI. And I intend to do so."

He pulled a pair of latex gloves and a handkerchief from his pocket.

"Don't mind me, Joseph. I don't like to get my hands dirty."

The old man had both hands to his neck as if he could coax more air through his throat. "Who do you work for?" he wheezed.

"I work for the people, of course." Parker smiled. "And for myself."

He shoved the handkerchief into the old man's mouth, pushed him forward until his head rested on the desk, and held him there until all movement stopped. Then he removed the cloth, used a second one to wipe everything down, then stooped to pick up the e-cigarette. The items went into a small bag he put back in his pocket.

He looked around and smiled.

"Dust to dust, Uncle Joe," he said to the dead man. "Very environmentally friendly. I hope your son will be happy."

-END-

From the Author

Thanks for reading *Freeze Before Burning*. I hope you'll take a moment to leave a review on Amazon, Goodreads, or any other social media you frequent. That way, I can connect to even more readers who are looking for books like mine.

With this book, I feel I can lay claim to a legitimate series. To that end, I've had all the covers redesigned to present a unified theme. My goal is to have everyone see the three books as distinct stand-alone stories but also a part of a continuing narrative.

Sam Tate is, of course, the anchor. As I've grown to know her, she's grown as a person. She has, I hope, a bright future ahead of her. I may give her a little time to adjust to her new life. Or I may come up with an idea and start on the next book sooner than I anticipated.

Meanwhile, book two, *Bird in Hand*, is doing well. Who doesn't like pirates? The book has received its share of accolades last year. Shelf Unbound named it a 2020 Best Indie Book and it also became a Next Generation Book Awards finalist.

My book total is up to six now, along with countless essays, some of which you can read at nikkistern.com. Type the address or scan the QR code.

I'm still on Facebook, Instagram, and Twitter, the last two as @realnikkistern. Come visit.

Also by Nikki Stern

Because I Say So
Hope in Small Doses
The Former Assassin
The Wedding Crasher
Bird in Hand

Made in the USA
Middletown, DE
01 April 2022